NEW YORK STATE PARKS BUCKET JOURNAL

Visit 177 State Parks in New York, USA

This book belongs to

_____

If found please call

_____

"**I only went out** for a walk, and finally concluded to stay out till sundown, for going out, I found, was really going in." ~John Muir

"**Must I tell you** that neither the Alps nor the Apennines, nor even Aetna itself, have dimmed, in my eyes, the beauty of our Catskills." ~ Thomas Cole

"**The joy of life** comes from our encounters with new experiences, and hence there is no greater joy than to have an endlessly changing horizon, for each day to have a new and different sun." " Chris McCandless

NEW YORK STATE PARKS BUCKET JOURNAL

The State of New York is a cascading landscape of glacier cut rolling hills, rivers, and canyons, and has approximately 900 waterfalls to visit in the central and finger lakes region. This state has enough forest for about one acre of trees per resident!

This breathtakingly diverse scenery encourages everyone who visits (or lives there) to get out and explore.

Some of the parks in the journal are well known and some are less traveled, all are waiting for you to discover their unique qualities.

In this New York State Parks Bucket Journal, **you will find individual pages for 177 state parks, recreation areas, and preserves** in the beautiful state of New York. Many allow for overnight camping and all are great for day use trips.

This bucket journal is different. It gives you the ability to create your own unique exploration of whichever state park site you choose

How to Use Your New York State Parks Bucket Journal

Parks that offer camping or other accommodations are on blue pages.
- Search out details about the state park or recreational site by using the website URL provided.
- Have fun planning the things you want to see on the left side of the 2-page spread.
- This is best done before you take your trip but can be done while you are out exploring.
- On the right side, chronicle everything that you do and experience. Included is space for journaling and reflection about your stay in the park.

Parks that are Day Use Area Only are on teal pages.
- Day-use parks are still fun to visit, even if you can't sleep there.
- Visit them when you are staying at other overnight parks or use them as day trip excursions to get out and explore.

The New York State Parks Bucket Journal will become a living memory for your trips and adventures as you discover the wonders of the state.

Enjoy exploring the beauty that is New York!

TABLE OF CONTENTS

RA: *Recreation Area Area* SMP: *State Marine Park* SP: *State Park* SPP: *State Park Preserve*

TABLE OF CONTENTS

RA: *Recreation Area Area* SMP: *State Marine Park* SP: *State Park* SPP: *State Park Preserve*

TABLE OF CONTENTS

RA: Recreation Area Area SMP: *State Marine Park* SP: *State Park* SPP: *State Park Preserve*

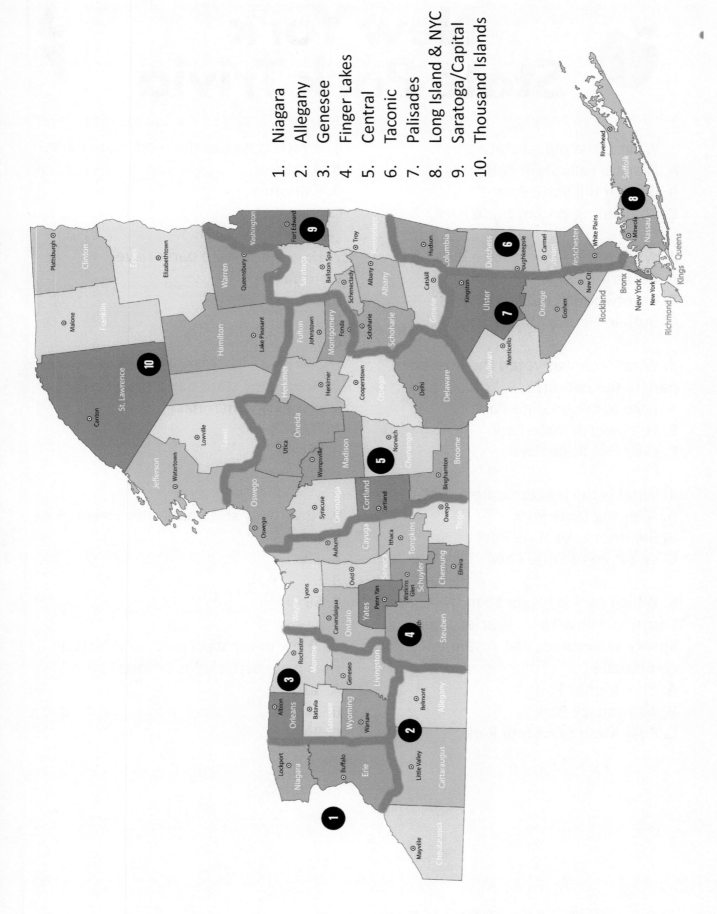

1. Niagara
2. Allegany
3. Genesee
4. Finger Lakes
5. Central
6. Taconic
7. Palisades
8. Long Island & NYC
9. Saratoga/Capital
10. Thousand Islands

New York State Park Trivia

1. What is the oldest state park?
A. Niagara Falls State Park
B. Golden Hill State Park
C. Cold Spring Harbor State Park

2. What is the newest state park?
A. Buttermilk Falls State Park
B. Brentwood State Park
C. Buffalo Harbor State Park

3. What park was voted the best state park in the nation?
A. Lake Superior State Park
B. Letchworth State Park
C. Lake Erie State Park

4. What is the biggest state park?
A. Allegany State Park
B. Belmont Lake State Park
C. Cedar Point State Park

5. Which park is bigger than the Grand Canyon, Yellowstone, Glacier, Great Smoky Mountains, and Yosemite combined?
A. Christopher Park
B. Adirondack Park
C. Bear Mountain State Park

6. Which state has the most state parks?
A. Alaska
B. California
C. New York

7. How many state parks have waterfalls?
A. 13
B. 15
C. 20

8. How many state parks have boat launches and marinas?
A. 67
B. 80
C. 75

9. How many state parks have swimming beaches?
A. 63
B. 67
C. 59

10. How many state parks and historic sites have battlefields or forts?
A. 12
B. 14
C. 9

Key: 1=A, 2=C, 3=B 4=A, 5=B, 6=C, 7=A, 8=C, 9=B, 10=A

Thousand Islands Region

- Clinton County
- Jefferson County
- Lewis County
- St. Lawrence County

Cumberland Bay State Park
City: Plattsburgh   County: Clinton

Plan your trip: https://parks.ny.gov/parks/cumberlandbay/details.aspx

Activities:

- ☐ Biking
- ☐ Boating
- ☐ Canoeing
- ☐ Disc Golf
- ☐ Fishing / Ice
- ☐ Hiking
- ☐ Horseback Riding
- ☐ Hunting
- ☐ Kayaking
- ☐ Marina
- ☐ Nature Center / Trails

- ☐ Photography
- ☐ Playing Fields
- ☐ Scenic Views
- ☐ Swimming
- ☐ Waterfalls
- ☐ Wildlife & Birding
- ☐ Winter Sports
- ☐
- ☐
- ☐
- ☐

Facilities:

- ☐ ADA
- ☐ Picnic sites
- ☐ Restrooms
- ☐ Showers
- ☐ Trailer Access
- ☐ Visitor center

- ☐ Group Camping
- ☐ RV Camp
- ☐ Rustic Camping
- ☐ Cabins / Yurts
- ☐ Day Use Area
- ☐

Notes:

Get the Facts

- ☐ Phone   (518) 563-5240
- ☐ Park Hours

  _____

- ☐ Reservations? ____Y ____N

  date made_____

- ☐ Open all year ____Y_____N

  dates_____

- ☐ Check in time _____
- ☐ Check out time _____
- ☐ Pet friendly _____Y _____N
- ☐ Max RV length _____
- ☐ Distance from home

  miles: _____

  hours: _____

- ☐ Address_____

  _____

  _____

Fees:

- ☐ Day Use $ _____
- ☐ Camp Sites $ _____
- ☐ RV Sites $ _____
- ☐ Refund policy

  _____

  _____

  _____

Make It Personal

Trip dates: _____ | The weather was: Sunny Cloudy Rainy Stormy Snowy Foggy Warm Cold

_____

Why I went:

_____

_____

How I got there: (circle all that apply) Plane Train Car Bus Bike Hike RV MC

_____

I went with:

_____

We stayed in (space, cabin # etc):

_____

Most relaxing day:

_____

_____

Something funny:

_____

_____

Someone we met:

_____

_____

Best story told:

_____

_____

The kids liked this:

_____

_____

The best food:

_____

_____

Games played:

_____

_____

Something disappointing:

_____

_____

Next time I'll do this differently:

_____

_____

Macomb Reservation State Park
City: Schuyler Falls   County: Clinton

Plan your trip: https://parks.ny.gov/parks/macombreservation/details.aspx

Activities:

- ❑ Biking
- ❑ Boating
- ❑ Canoeing
- ❑ Disc Golf
- ❑ Fishing / Ice
- ❑ Hiking
- ❑ Horseback Riding
- ❑ Hunting
- ❑ Kayaking
- ❑ Marina
- ❑ Nature Center / Trails

- ❑ Photography
- ❑ Playing Fields
- ❑ Scenic Views
- ❑ Swimming
- ❑ Waterfalls
- ❑ Wildlife & Birding
- ❑ Winter Sports
- ❑
- ❑
- ❑
- ❑

Facilities:

- ❑ ADA
- ❑ Picnic sites
- ❑ Restrooms
- ❑ Showers
- ❑ Trailer Access
- ❑ Visitor center

- ❑ Group Camping
- ❑ RV Camp
- ❑ Rustic Camping
- ❑ Cabins / Yurts
- ❑ Day Use Area
- ❑

Notes:

Get the Facts

- ❑ Phone   (518) 643-9952
- ❑ Park Hours

  _____

- ❑ Reservations? _____Y _____N

  date made_____

- ❑ Open all year _____Y _____N

  dates_____

- ❑ Check in time _____
- ❑ Check out time _____
- ❑ Pet friendly _____Y _____N
- ❑ Max RV length _____
- ❑ Distance from home

  miles: _____

  hours: _____

- ❑ Address_____

  _____

  _____

Fees:

- ❑ Day Use $ _____
- ❑ Camp Sites $ _____
- ❑ RV Sites $ _____
- ❑ Refund policy

  _____

  _____

  _____

Make It Personal

Trip dates: _____ | The weather was: Sunny Cloudy Rainy Stormy Snowy Foggy Warm Cold

Why I went:
_____

_____

How I got there: (circle all that apply)   Plane   Train   Car   Bus   Bike   Hike   RV   MC
_____

I went with:
_____

We stayed in (space, cabin # etc):
_____

Most relaxing day:
_____

_____

Something funny:
_____

_____

Someone we met:
_____

_____

Best story told:
_____

_____

The kids liked this:
_____

_____

The best food:
_____

_____

Games played:
_____

_____

Something disappointing:
_____

_____

Next time I'll do this differently:
_____

_____

Mary Island State Park
City: 1000 Islands   County: Jefferson

Plan your trip: https://parks.ny.gov/parks/maryisland/details.aspx

Activities:

- ❑ Biking
- ❑ Boating
- ❑ Canoeing
- ❑ Disc Golf
- ❑ Fishing / Ice
- ❑ Hiking
- ❑ Horseback Riding
- ❑ Hunting
- ❑ Kayaking
- ❑ Marina
- ❑ Nature Center / Trails

- ❑ Photography
- ❑ Playing Fields
- ❑ Scenic Views
- ❑ Swimming
- ❑ Waterfalls
- ❑ Wildlife & Birding
- ❑ Winter Sports
- ❑
- ❑
- ❑
- ❑

Facilities:

- ❑ ADA
- ❑ Picnic sites
- ❑ Restrooms
- ❑ Showers
- ❑ Trailer Access
- ❑ Visitor center

- ❑ Group Camping
- ❑ RV Camp
- ❑ Rustic Camping
- ❑ Cabins / Yurts
- ❑ Day Use Area
- ❑

Notes:

Get the Facts

- ❑ Phone   (315) 482-9381
- ❑ Park Hours

  _____

- ❑ Reservations? ____Y ____N

  date made_____

- ❑ Open all year ____Y_____N

  dates_____

- ❑ Check in time _____
- ❑ Check out time _____
- ❑ Pet friendly _____Y _____N
- ❑ Max RV length _____
- ❑ Distance from home

  miles: _____

  hours: _____

- ❑ Address_____

  _____

  _____

Fees:

- ❑ Day Use $ _____
- ❑ Camp Sites $ _____
- ❑ RV Sites $ _____
- ❑ Refund policy

  _____

  _____

  _____

Make It Personal

Trip dates: _____ | The weather was: Sunny   Cloudy   Rainy   Stormy   Snowy   Foggy   Warm   Cold

Why I went:
_____

_____

How I got there: (circle all that apply)   Plane   Train   Car   Bus   Bike   Hike   RV   MC
_____

I went with:
_____

We stayed in (space, cabin # etc):
_____

Most relaxing day:
_____

Something funny:
_____

Someone we met:
_____

Best story told:
_____

The kids liked this:
_____

The best food:
_____

Games played:
_____

Something disappointing:
_____

Next time I'll do this differently:
_____

_____

Grass Point State Park
City: Alexandria Bay   County: Jefferson

Plan your trip: https://parks.ny.gov/parks/grasspoint/details.aspx

Activities:

- ❏ Biking
- ❏ Boating
- ❏ Canoeing
- ❏ Disc Golf
- ❏ Fishing / Ice
- ❏ Hiking
- ❏ Horseback Riding
- ❏ Hunting
- ❏ Kayaking
- ❏ Marina
- ❏ Nature Center / Trails

- ❏ Photography
- ❏ Playing Fields
- ❏ Scenic Views
- ❏ Swimming
- ❏ Waterfalls
- ❏ Wildlife & Birding
- ❏ Winter Sports
- ❏
- ❏
- ❏
- ❏

Facilities:

- ❏ ADA
- ❏ Picnic sites
- ❏ Restrooms
- ❏ Showers
- ❏ Trailer Access
- ❏ Visitor center

- ❏ Group Camping
- ❏ RV Camp
- ❏ Rustic Camping
- ❏ Cabins / Yurts
- ❏ Day Use Area
- ❏

Notes:

Get the Facts

- ❏ Phone   (315) 686-4472
- ❏ Park Hours

  _____

- ❏ Reservations? ____Y ____N

  date made_____

- ❏ Open all year ____Y____N

  dates_____

- ❏ Check in time _____
- ❏ Check out time _____
- ❏ Pet friendly _____Y _____N
- ❏ Max RV length _____
- ❏ Distance from home

  miles: _____

  hours: _____

- ❏ Address_____

  _____

  _____

Fees:

- ❏ Day Use $ _____
- ❏ Camp Sites $ _____
- ❏ RV Sites $ _____
- ❏ Refund policy

  _____

  _____

  _____

Make It Personal

Trip dates: _____ | The weather was: Sunny Cloudy Rainy Stormy Snowy Foggy Warm Cold

Why I went:
_____

_____

How I got there: (circle all that apply) Plane   Train   Car   Bus   Bike   Hike   RV   MC
_____

I went with:
_____

We stayed in (space, cabin # etc):
_____

Most relaxing day:
_____

_____

Something funny:
_____

_____

Someone we met:
_____

_____

Best story told:
_____

_____

The kids liked this:
_____

_____

The best food:
_____

_____

Games played:
_____

_____

Something disappointing:
_____

_____

Next time I'll do this differently:
_____

_____

Keewaydin State Park
City: Alexandria Bay   County: Jefferson

Plan your trip: https://parks.ny.gov/parks/keewaydin/details.aspx

Activities:

- ❑ Biking
- ❑ Boating
- ❑ Canoeing
- ❑ Disc Golf
- ❑ Fishing / Ice
- ❑ Hiking
- ❑ Horseback Riding
- ❑ Hunting
- ❑ Kayaking
- ❑ Marina
- ❑ Nature Center / Trails

- ❑ Photography
- ❑ Playing Fields
- ❑ Scenic Views
- ❑ Swimming
- ❑ Waterfalls
- ❑ Wildlife & Birding
- ❑ Winter Sports
- ❑
- ❑
- ❑
- ❑

Facilities:

- ❑ ADA
- ❑ Picnic sites
- ❑ Restrooms
- ❑ Showers
- ❑ Trailer Access
- ❑ Visitor center

- ❑ Group Camping
- ❑ RV Camp
- ❑ Rustic Camping
- ❑ Cabins / Yurts
- ❑ Day Use Area
- ❑

Notes:

Get the Facts

- ❑ Phone   (315) 482-3331
- ❑ Park Hours

  _____

- ❑ Reservations? _____Y _____N

  date made_____

- ❑ Open all year _____Y_____N

  dates_____

- ❑ Check in time _____
- ❑ Check out time _____
- ❑ Pet friendly _____Y _____N
- ❑ Max RV length _____
- ❑ Distance from home

  miles: _____

  hours: _____

- ❑ Address_____

  _____

  _____

Fees:

- ❑ Day Use $ _____
- ❑ Camp Sites $ _____
- ❑ RV Sites $ _____
- ❑ Refund policy

  _____

  _____

  _____

Make It Personal

Trip dates: _____ | The weather was: Sunny Cloudy Rainy Stormy Snowy Foggy Warm Cold

Why I went:

_____

_____

How I got there: (circle all that apply) Plane Train Car Bus Bike Hike RV MC

I went with:

_____

We stayed in (space, cabin # etc):

_____

Most relaxing day:

_____

_____

Something funny:

_____

_____

Someone we met:

_____

_____

Best story told:

_____

_____

The kids liked this:

_____

_____

The best food:

_____

_____

Games played:

_____

_____

Something disappointing:

_____

_____

Next time I'll do this differently:

_____

_____

Burnham Paint State Park
City: Cape Vincent   County: Jefferson

Plan your trip: https://parks.ny.gov/parks/burnhampoint/details.aspx

Activities:

- ❑ Biking
- ❑ Boating
- ❑ Canoeing
- ❑ Disc Golf
- ❑ Fishing / Ice
- ❑ Hiking
- ❑ Horseback Riding
- ❑ Hunting
- ❑ Kayaking
- ❑ Marina
- ❑ Nature Center / Trails
- ❑ Photography
- ❑ Playing Fields
- ❑ Scenic Views
- ❑ Swimming
- ❑ Waterfalls
- ❑ Wildlife & Birding
- ❑ Winter Sports
- ❑
- ❑
- ❑
- ❑

Facilities:

- ❑ ADA
- ❑ Picnic sites
- ❑ Restrooms
- ❑ Showers
- ❑ Trailer Access
- ❑ Visitor center
- ❑ Group Camping
- ❑ RV Camp
- ❑ Rustic Camping
- ❑ Cabins / Yurts
- ❑ Day Use Area
- ❑

Notes:

Get the Facts

- ❑ Phone   (315) 654-2522
- ❑ Park Hours

_____

- ❑ Reservations? _____Y _____N

date made_____

- ❑ Open all year _____Y_____N

dates_____

- ❑ Check in time _____
- ❑ Check out time _____
- ❑ Pet friendly _____Y _____N
- ❑ Max RV length _____
- ❑ Distance from home

miles: _____

hours: _____

- ❑ Address_____

_____

_____

Fees:

- ❑ Day Use $ _____
- ❑ Camp Sites $ _____
- ❑ RV Sites $ _____
- ❑ Refund policy

_____

_____

_____

Make It Personal

Trip dates: _____ | The weather was: Sunny Cloudy Rainy Stormy Snowy Foggy Warm Cold

Why I went: _____

_____

How I got there: (circle all that apply) Plane Train Car Bus Bike Hike RV MC

I went with: _____

We stayed in (space, cabin # etc): _____

Most relaxing day: _____

_____

Something funny: _____

_____

Someone we met: _____

_____

Best story told: _____

_____

The kids liked this: _____

_____

The best food: _____

_____

Games played: _____

_____

Something disappointing: _____

_____

Next time I'll do this differently: _____

_____

Canoe-Picnic Point State Park
City: Clayton   County: Jefferson

Plan your trip: https://parks.ny.gov/parks/canoepicnicpoint/details.aspx

Activities:

- ❏ Biking
- ❏ Boating
- ❏ Canoeing
- ❏ Disc Golf
- ❏ Fishing / Ice
- ❏ Hiking
- ❏ Horseback Riding
- ❏ Hunting
- ❏ Kayaking
- ❏ Marina
- ❏ Nature Center / Trails
- ❏ Photography
- ❏ Playing Fields
- ❏ Scenic Views
- ❏ Swimming
- ❏ Waterfalls
- ❏ Wildlife & Birding
- ❏ Winter Sports
- ❏
- ❏
- ❏
- ❏

Facilities:

- ❏ ADA
- ❏ Picnic sites
- ❏ Restrooms
- ❏ Showers
- ❏ Trailer Access
- ❏ Visitor center
- ❏ Group Camping
- ❏ RV Camp
- ❏ Rustic Camping
- ❏ Cabins / Yurts
- ❏ Day Use Area
- ❏

Notes:

Get the Facts

- ❏ Phone   (315) 654-2522
- ❏ Park Hours

  _____

- ❏ Reservations? ____Y ____N

  date made_____

- ❏ Open all year ____Y____N

  dates_____

- ❏ Check in time _____
- ❏ Check out time _____
- ❏ Pet friendly _____Y _____N
- ❏ Max RV length _____
- ❏ Distance from home

  miles: _____

  hours: _____

- ❏ Address_____

  _____

  _____

Fees:

- ❏ Day Use $ _____
- ❏ Camp Sites $ _____
- ❏ RV Sites $ _____
- ❏ Refund policy

  _____

  _____

  _____

Make It Personal

Trip dates: _____ | The weather was: Sunny   Cloudy   Rainy   Stormy   Snowy   Foggy   Warm   Cold

Why I went:
_____

_____

How I got there: (circle all that apply)   Plane   Train   Car   Bus   Bike   Hike   RV   MC

I went with:
_____

We stayed in (space, cabin # etc):
_____

Most relaxing day:
_____

_____

Something funny:
_____

_____

Someone we met:
_____

_____

Best story told:
_____

_____

The kids liked this:
_____

_____

The best food:
_____

_____

Games played:
_____

_____

Something disappointing:
_____

_____

Next time I'll do this differently:
_____

_____

Cedar Point State Park
City: Clayton   County: Jefferson

Plan your trip: https://parks.ny.gov/parks/cedarpoint/details.aspx

Activities:

- ❑ Biking
- ❑ Boating
- ❑ Canoeing
- ❑ Disc Golf
- ❑ Fishing / Ice
- ❑ Hiking
- ❑ Horseback Riding
- ❑ Hunting
- ❑ Kayaking
- ❑ Marina
- ❑ Nature Center / Trails

- ❑ Photography
- ❑ Playing Fields
- ❑ Scenic Views
- ❑ Swimming
- ❑ Waterfalls
- ❑ Wildlife & Birding
- ❑ Winter Sports
- ❑
- ❑
- ❑
- ❑

Facilities:

- ❑ ADA
- ❑ Picnic sites
- ❑ Restrooms
- ❑ Showers
- ❑ Trailer Access
- ❑ Visitor center

- ❑ Group Camping
- ❑ RV Camp
- ❑ Rustic Camping
- ❑ Cabins / Yurts
- ❑ Day Use Area
- ❑

Notes:

Get the Facts

- ❑ Phone (315) 654-2522
- ❑ Park Hours

  _____
- ❑ Reservations? ____Y ____N

  date made_____
- ❑ Open all year ____Y____N

  dates_____
- ❑ Check in time _____
- ❑ Check out time _____
- ❑ Pet friendly ____Y ____N
- ❑ Max RV length _____
- ❑ Distance from home

  miles: _____

  hours: _____
- ❑ Address_____

  _____

  _____

Fees:

- ❑ Day Use $ _____
- ❑ Camp Sites $ _____
- ❑ RV Sites $ _____
- ❑ Refund policy

  _____

  _____

  _____

Make It Personal

Trip dates: _____ | The weather was: Sunny Cloudy Rainy Stormy Snowy Foggy Warm Cold

Why I went:
_____

_____

How I got there: (circle all that apply)   Plane   Train   Car   Bus   Bike   Hike   RV   MC
_____

I went with:
_____

We stayed in (space, cabin # etc):
_____

Most relaxing day:
_____

_____

Something funny:
_____

_____

Someone we met:
_____

_____

Best story told:
_____

_____

The kids liked this:
_____

_____

The best food:
_____

_____

Games played:
_____

_____

Something disappointing:
_____

_____

Next time I'll do this differently:
_____

_____

Dewolf Point State Park
City: Fineview   County: Jefferson

Plan your trip: https://parks.ny.gov/parks/dewolfpoint/details.aspx

Activities:

- ❑ Biking
- ❑ Boating
- ❑ Canoeing
- ❑ Disc Golf
- ❑ Fishing / Ice
- ❑ Hiking
- ❑ Horseback Riding
- ❑ Hunting
- ❑ Kayaking
- ❑ Marina
- ❑ Nature Center / Trails

- ❑ Photography
- ❑ Playing Fields
- ❑ Scenic Views
- ❑ Swimming
- ❑ Waterfalls
- ❑ Wildlife & Birding
- ❑ Winter Sports
- ❑
- ❑
- ❑
- ❑

Facilities:

- ❑ ADA
- ❑ Picnic sites
- ❑ Restrooms
- ❑ Showers
- ❑ Trailer Access
- ❑ Visitor center

- ❑ Group Camping
- ❑ RV Camp
- ❑ Rustic Camping
- ❑ Cabins / Yurts
- ❑ Day Use Area
- ❑

Notes:

Get the Facts

- ❑ Phone   (315) 482-2012
- ❑ Park Hours

  _____

- ❑ Reservations? ____Y ____N

  date made_____

- ❑ Open all year ____Y_____N

  dates_____

- ❑ Check in time _____
- ❑ Check out time _____
- ❑ Pet friendly _____Y _____N
- ❑ Max RV length _____
- ❑ Distance from home

  miles: _____

  hours: _____

- ❑ Address_____

  _____

  _____

Fees:

- ❑ Day Use $ _____
- ❑ Camp Sites $ _____
- ❑ RV Sites $ _____
- ❑ Refund policy

  _____

  _____

  _____

Make It Personal

Trip dates: _____ | The weather was: Sunny Cloudy Rainy Stormy Snowy Foggy Warm Cold

Why I went: _____

_____

How I got there: (circle all that apply) Plane Train Car Bus Bike Hike RV MC

I went with: _____

We stayed in (space, cabin # etc): _____

Most relaxing day: _____

_____

Something funny: _____

_____

Someone we met: _____

_____

Best story told: _____

_____

The kids liked this: _____

_____

The best food: _____

_____

Games played: _____

_____

Something disappointing: _____

_____

Next time I'll do this differently: _____

_____

Wellesley Island State Park
City: Fineview   County: Jefferson

Plan your trip: https://parks.ny.gov/parks/wellesleyisland/details.aspx

Activities:

- ❏ Biking
- ❏ Boating
- ❏ Canoeing
- ❏ Disc Golf
- ❏ Fishing / Ice
- ❏ Hiking
- ❏ Horseback Riding
- ❏ Hunting
- ❏ Kayaking
- ❏ Marina
- ❏ Nature Center / Trails

- ❏ Photography
- ❏ Playing Fields
- ❏ Scenic Views
- ❏ Swimming
- ❏ Waterfalls
- ❏ Wildlife & Birding
- ❏ Winter Sports
- ❏
- ❏
- ❏
- ❏

Facilities:

- ❏ ADA
- ❏ Picnic sites
- ❏ Restrooms
- ❏ Showers
- ❏ Trailer Access
- ❏ Visitor center

- ❏ Group Camping
- ❏ RV Camp
- ❏ Rustic Camping
- ❏ Cabins / Yurts
- ❏ Day Use Area
- ❏

Notes:

Get the Facts

- ❏ Phone   (315) 482-2722
- ❏ Park Hours

  _____

- ❏ Reservations? ____Y ____N

  date made_____

- ❏ Open all year ____Y____N

  dates_____

- ❏ Check in time _____
- ❏ Check out time _____
- ❏ Pet friendly _____Y _____N
- ❏ Max RV length _____
- ❏ Distance from home

  miles: _____

  hours: _____

- ❏ Address_____

  _____

  _____

Fees:

- ❏ Day Use $ _____
- ❏ Camp Sites $ _____
- ❏ RV Sites $ _____
- ❏ Refund policy

  _____

  _____

  _____

Make It Personal

Trip dates: _____ | The weather was: Sunny Cloudy Rainy Stormy Snowy Foggy Warm Cold

Why I went: _____

_____

How I got there: (circle all that apply)   Plane   Train   Car   Bus   Bike   Hike   RV   MC

I went with: _____

We stayed in (space, cabin # etc): _____

Most relaxing day: _____

_____

Something funny: _____

_____

Someone we met: _____

_____

Best story told: _____

_____

The kids liked this: _____

_____

The best food: _____

_____

Games played: _____

_____

Something disappointing: _____

_____

Next time I'll do this differently: _____

_____

Robert G. Wehle State Park
City: Henderson   County: Jefferson

Plan your trip: https://parks.ny.gov/parks/robertwhele/details.aspx

Activities:

- ❏ Biking
- ❏ Boating
- ❏ Canoeing
- ❏ Disc Golf
- ❏ Fishing / Ice
- ❏ Hiking
- ❏ Horseback Riding
- ❏ Hunting
- ❏ Kayaking
- ❏ Marina
- ❏ Nature Center / Trails
- ❏ Photography
- ❏ Playing Fields
- ❏ Scenic Views
- ❏ Swimming
- ❏ Waterfalls
- ❏ Wildlife & Birding
- ❏ Winter Sports
- ❏
- ❏
- ❏
- ❏

Facilities:

- ❏ ADA
- ❏ Picnic sites
- ❏ Restrooms
- ❏ Showers
- ❏ Trailer Access
- ❏ Visitor center
- ❏ Group Camping
- ❏ RV Camp
- ❏ Rustic Camping
- ❏ Cabins / Yurts
- ❏ Day Use Area
- ❏

Notes:

Get the Facts

- ❏ Phone   (315) 938-5302
- ❏ Park Hours

  _____

- ❏ Reservations? ____Y ____N

  date made_____

- ❏ Open all year ____Y____N

  dates_____

- ❏ Check in time _____
- ❏ Check out time _____
- ❏ Pet friendly _____Y _____N
- ❏ Max RV length _____
- ❏ Distance from home

  miles: _____

  hours: _____

- ❏ Address_____

  _____

  _____

Fees:

- ❏ Day Use $ _____
- ❏ Camp Sites $ _____
- ❏ RV Sites $ _____
- ❏ Refund policy

  _____

  _____

  _____

Make It Personal

Trip dates: _____ | The weather was: Sunny Cloudy Rainy Stormy Snowy Foggy Warm Cold

Why I went: _____

_____

How I got there: (circle all that apply) Plane Train Car Bus Bike Hike RV MC

I went with: _____

We stayed in (space, cabin # etc): _____

Most relaxing day: _____

_____

Something funny: _____

_____

Someone we met: _____

_____

Best story told: _____

_____

The kids liked this: _____

_____

The best food: _____

_____

Games played: _____

_____

Something disappointing: _____

_____

Next time I'll do this differently: _____

_____

Southwick Beach State Park

City: Henderson   **County: Jefferson**

Plan your trip: https://parks.ny.gov/parks/southwickbeach/details.aspx

Activities:

- ❑ Biking
- ❑ Boating
- ❑ Canoeing
- ❑ Disc Golf
- ❑ Fishing / Ice
- ❑ Hiking
- ❑ Horseback Riding
- ❑ Hunting
- ❑ Kayaking
- ❑ Marina
- ❑ Nature Center / Trails

- ❑ Photography
- ❑ Playing Fields
- ❑ Scenic Views
- ❑ Swimming
- ❑ Waterfalls
- ❑ Wildlife & Birding
- ❑ Winter Sports
- ❑
- ❑
- ❑
- ❑

Facilities:

- ❑ ADA
- ❑ Picnic sites
- ❑ Restrooms
- ❑ Showers
- ❑ Trailer Access
- ❑ Visitor center

- ❑ Group Camping
- ❑ RV Camp
- ❑ Rustic Camping
- ❑ Cabins / Yurts
- ❑ Day Use Area
- ❑

Notes:

Get the Facts

- ❑ Phone   (315) 846-5338
- ❑ Park Hours

_____

- ❑ Reservations? _____Y _____N

date made_____

- ❑ Open all year _____Y _____N

dates_____

- ❑ Check in time _____
- ❑ Check out time _____
- ❑ Pet friendly _____Y _____N
- ❑ Max RV length _____
- ❑ Distance from home

miles: _____

hours: _____

- ❑ Address_____

_____

_____

Fees:

- ❑ Day Use $ _____
- ❑ Camp Sites $ _____
- ❑ RV Sites $ _____
- ❑ Refund policy

_____

_____

_____

Make It Personal

Trip dates: _____ | The weather was: Sunny Cloudy Rainy Stormy Snowy Foggy Warm Cold

Why I went:
_____

How I got there: (circle all that apply)   Plane   Train   Car   Bus   Bike   Hike   RV   MC
_____

I went with:
_____

We stayed in (space, cabin # etc):
_____

Most relaxing day:
_____

Something funny:
_____

Someone we met:
_____

Best story told:
_____

The kids liked this:
_____

The best food:
_____

Games played:
_____

Something disappointing:
_____

Next time I'll do this differently:
_____
_____

Westcott Beach State Park
City: Henderson   County: Jefferson

Plan your trip: https://parks.ny.gov/parks/westcottbeach/details.aspx

Activities:

- ❑ Biking
- ❑ Boating
- ❑ Canoeing
- ❑ Disc Golf
- ❑ Fishing / Ice
- ❑ Hiking
- ❑ Horseback Riding
- ❑ Hunting
- ❑ Kayaking
- ❑ Marina
- ❑ Nature Center / Trails

- ❑ Photography
- ❑ Playing Fields
- ❑ Scenic Views
- ❑ Swimming
- ❑ Waterfalls
- ❑ Wildlife & Birding
- ❑ Winter Sports
- ❑
- ❑
- ❑
- ❑

Facilities:

- ❑ ADA
- ❑ Picnic sites
- ❑ Restrooms
- ❑ Showers
- ❑ Trailer Access
- ❑ Visitor center

- ❑ Group Camping
- ❑ RV Camp
- ❑ Rustic Camping
- ❑ Cabins / Yurts
- ❑ Day Use Area
- ❑

Notes:

Get the Facts

- ❑ Phone   (315) 646-2239
- ❑ Park Hours

_____

- ❑ Reservations? ____Y ____N

date made_____

- ❑ Open all year ____Y ____N

dates_____

- ❑ Check in time _____
- ❑ Check out time _____
- ❑ Pet friendly _____Y ____N
- ❑ Max RV length _____
- ❑ Distance from home

miles: _____

hours: _____

- ❑ Address_____

_____

_____

Fees:

- ❑ Day Use $ _____
- ❑ Camp Sites $ _____
- ❑ RV Sites $ _____
- ❑ Refund policy

_____

_____

_____

Make It Personal

Trip dates: _____ | The weather was: Sunny Cloudy Rainy Stormy Snowy Foggy Warm Cold

Why I went:
_____

_____

How I got there: (circle all that apply)   Plane   Train   Car   Bus   Bike   Hike   RV   MC
_____

I went with:
_____

We stayed in (space, cabin # etc):
_____

Most relaxing day:
_____

_____

Something funny:
_____

_____

Someone we met:
_____

_____

Best story told:
_____

_____

The kids liked this:
_____

_____

The best food:
_____

_____

Games played:
_____

_____

Something disappointing:
_____

_____

Next time I'll do this differently:
_____

_____

Kring Point State Park
City: Redwood   County: Jefferson

Plan your trip: https://parks.ny.gov/parks/kringpoint/details.aspx

Activities:

- ❑ Biking
- ❑ Boating
- ❑ Canoeing
- ❑ Disc Golf
- ❑ Fishing / Ice
- ❑ Hiking
- ❑ Horseback Riding
- ❑ Hunting
- ❑ Kayaking
- ❑ Marina
- ❑ Nature Center / Trails

- ❑ Photography
- ❑ Playing Fields
- ❑ Scenic Views
- ❑ Swimming
- ❑ Waterfalls
- ❑ Wildlife & Birding
- ❑ Winter Sports
- ❑
- ❑
- ❑
- ❑

Facilities:

- ❑ ADA
- ❑ Picnic sites
- ❑ Restrooms
- ❑ Showers
- ❑ Trailer Access
- ❑ Visitor center

- ❑ Group Camping
- ❑ RV Camp
- ❑ Rustic Camping
- ❑ Cabins / Yurts
- ❑ Day Use Area
- ❑

Notes:

Get the Facts

- ❑ Phone   (315) 482-2444
- ❑ Park Hours

  _____

- ❑ Reservations? ____Y ____N

  date made_____

- ❑ Open all year ____Y____N

  dates_____

- ❑ Check in time _____
- ❑ Check out time _____
- ❑ Pet friendly _____Y _____N
- ❑ Max RV length _____
- ❑ Distance from home

  miles: _____

  hours: _____

- ❑ Address_____

  _____

  _____

Fees:

- ❑ Day Use $ _____
- ❑ Camp Sites $ _____
- ❑ RV Sites $ _____
- ❑ Refund policy

  _____

  _____

  _____

Make It Personal

Trip dates: _____ | The weather was: Sunny Cloudy Rainy Stormy Snowy Foggy Warm Cold

Why I went:
_____

_____

How I got there: (circle all that apply)   Plane   Train   Car   Bus   Bike   Hike   RV   MC
_____

I went with:
_____

We stayed in (space, cabin # etc):
_____

Most relaxing day:
_____

_____

Something funny:
_____

_____

Someone we met:
_____

_____

Best story told:
_____

_____

The kids liked this:
_____

_____

The best food:
_____

_____

Games played:
_____

_____

Something disappointing:
_____

_____

Next time I'll do this differently:
_____

_____

Long Point State Park - Thousand Islands
City: Three Mile Bay   County: Jefferson

Plan your trip: https://parks.ny.gov/parks/longpoint/details.aspx

Activities:

- ❑ Biking
- ❑ Boating
- ❑ Canoeing
- ❑ Disc Golf
- ❑ Fishing / Ice
- ❑ Hiking
- ❑ Horseback Riding
- ❑ Hunting
- ❑ Kayaking
- ❑ Marina
- ❑ Nature Center / Trails

- ❑ Photography
- ❑ Playing Fields
- ❑ Scenic Views
- ❑ Swimming
- ❑ Waterfalls
- ❑ Wildlife & Birding
- ❑ Winter Sports
- ❑
- ❑
- ❑
- ❑

Facilities:

- ❑ ADA
- ❑ Picnic sites
- ❑ Restrooms
- ❑ Showers
- ❑ Trailer Access
- ❑ Visitor center

- ❑ Group Camping
- ❑ RV Camp
- ❑ Rustic Camping
- ❑ Cabins / Yurts
- ❑ Day Use Area
- ❑

Notes:

Get the Facts

- ❑ Phone   (315) 649-5258
- ❑ Park Hours

  _____

- ❑ Reservations? ____Y ____N

  date made_____

- ❑ Open all year ____Y____N

  dates_____

- ❑ Check in time _____
- ❑ Check out time _____
- ❑ Pet friendly _____Y _____N
- ❑ Max RV length _____
- ❑ Distance from home

  miles: _____

  hours: _____

- ❑ Address_____

  _____

  _____

Fees:

- ❑ Day Use $ _____
- ❑ Camp Sites $ _____
- ❑ RV Sites $ _____
- ❑ Refund policy

  _____

  _____

  _____

Make It Personal

Trip dates: _____ | The weather was: Sunny Cloudy Rainy Stormy Snowy Foggy Warm Cold

Why I went: _____

_____

How I got there: (circle all that apply)   Plane   Train   Car   Bus   Bike   Hike   RV   MC
_____

I went with: _____

We stayed in (space, cabin # etc): _____

Most relaxing day: _____

_____

Something funny: _____

_____

Someone we met: _____

_____

Best story told: _____

_____

The kids liked this: _____

_____

The best food: _____

_____

Games played: _____

_____

Something disappointing: _____

_____

Next time I'll do this differently: _____

_____

Whetstone Gulf State Park
City: Lowville   County: Lewis

Plan your trip: https://parks.ny.gov/parks/whetstonegulf/details.aspx

Activities:

- ❑ Biking
- ❑ Boating
- ❑ Canoeing
- ❑ Disc Golf
- ❑ Fishing / Ice
- ❑ Hiking
- ❑ Horseback Riding
- ❑ Hunting
- ❑ Kayaking
- ❑ Marina
- ❑ Nature Center / Trails

- ❑ Photography
- ❑ Playing Fields
- ❑ Scenic Views
- ❑ Swimming
- ❑ Waterfalls
- ❑ Wildlife & Birding
- ❑ Winter Sports
- ❑
- ❑
- ❑
- ❑

Facilities:

- ❑ ADA
- ❑ Picnic sites
- ❑ Restrooms
- ❑ Showers
- ❑ Trailer Access
- ❑ Visitor center

- ❑ Group Camping
- ❑ RV Camp
- ❑ Rustic Camping
- ❑ Cabins / Yurts
- ❑ Day Use Area
- ❑

Notes:

Get the Facts

- ❑ Phone   (315) 376-6630
- ❑ Park Hours

_____

- ❑ Reservations? ____Y ____N

date made_____

- ❑ Open all year ____Y_____N

dates_____

- ❑ Check in time _____
- ❑ Check out time _____
- ❑ Pet friendly _____Y _____N
- ❑ Max RV length _____
- ❑ Distance from home

miles: _____

hours: _____

- ❑ Address_____

_____

_____

Fees:

- ❑ Day Use $ _____
- ❑ Camp Sites $ _____
- ❑ RV Sites $ _____
- ❑ Refund policy

_____

_____

_____

Make It Personal

Trip dates: _____ | The weather was: Sunny Cloudy Rainy Stormy Snowy Foggy Warm Cold

Why I went: _____

_____

How I got there: (circle all that apply) Plane Train Car Bus Bike Hike RV MC

_____

I went with: _____

We stayed in (space, cabin # etc): _____

Most relaxing day: _____

_____

Something funny: _____

_____

Someone we met: _____

_____

Best story told: _____

_____

The kids liked this: _____

_____

The best food: _____

_____

Games played: _____

_____

Something disappointing: _____

_____

Next time I'll do this differently: _____

_____

Higley Flow State Park
City: Colton   County: St. Lawrence

Plan your trip: https://parks.ny.gov/parks/higleyflow/details.aspx

Activities:

- ❑ Biking
- ❑ Boating
- ❑ Canoeing
- ❑ Disc Golf
- ❑ Fishing / Ice
- ❑ Hiking
- ❑ Horseback Riding
- ❑ Hunting
- ❑ Kayaking
- ❑ Marina
- ❑ Nature Center / Trails

- ❑ Photography
- ❑ Playing Fields
- ❑ Scenic Views
- ❑ Swimming
- ❑ Waterfalls
- ❑ Wildlife & Birding
- ❑ Winter Sports
- ❑
- ❑
- ❑
- ❑

Facilities:

- ❑ ADA
- ❑ Picnic sites
- ❑ Restrooms
- ❑ Showers
- ❑ Trailer Access
- ❑ Visitor center

- ❑ Group Camping
- ❑ RV Camp
- ❑ Rustic Camping
- ❑ Cabins / Yurts
- ❑ Day Use Area
- ❑

Notes:

Get the Facts

- ❑ Phone   (315) 262-2880
- ❑ Park Hours

  _____

- ❑ Reservations? ____Y ____N

  date made_____

- ❑ Open all year ____Y____N

  dates_____

- ❑ Check in time _____
- ❑ Check out time _____
- ❑ Pet friendly _____Y _____N
- ❑ Max RV length _____
- ❑ Distance from home

  miles: _____

  hours: _____

- ❑ Address_____

  _____

  _____

Fees:

- ❑ Day Use $ _____
- ❑ Camp Sites $ _____
- ❑ RV Sites $ _____
- ❑ Refund policy

  _____

  _____

  _____

Make It Personal

Trip dates: _____ | The weather was: Sunny Cloudy Rainy Stormy Snowy Foggy Warm Cold

Why I went:
_____

_____

How I got there: (circle all that apply)   Plane   Train   Car   Bus   Bike   Hike   RV   MC
_____

I went with:
_____

We stayed in (space, cabin # etc):
_____

Most relaxing day:
_____

_____

Something funny:
_____

_____

Someone we met:
_____

_____

Best story told:
_____

_____

The kids liked this:
_____

_____

The best food:
_____

_____

Games played:
_____

_____

Something disappointing:
_____

_____

Next time I'll do this differently:
_____

_____

Cedar Island State Park
City: Hammond   County: St. Lawrence

Plan your trip: https://parks.ny.gov/parks/cedarisland/details.aspx

Activities:

- ❑ Biking
- ❑ Boating
- ❑ Canoeing
- ❑ Disc Golf
- ❑ Fishing / Ice
- ❑ Hiking
- ❑ Horseback Riding
- ❑ Hunting
- ❑ Kayaking
- ❑ Marina
- ❑ Nature Center / Trails

- ❑ Photography
- ❑ Playing Fields
- ❑ Scenic Views
- ❑ Swimming
- ❑ Waterfalls
- ❑ Wildlife & Birding
- ❑ Winter Sports
- ❑
- ❑
- ❑
- ❑

Facilities:

- ❑ ADA
- ❑ Picnic sites
- ❑ Restrooms
- ❑ Showers
- ❑ Trailer Access
- ❑ Visitor center

- ❑ Group Camping
- ❑ RV Camp
- ❑ Rustic Camping
- ❑ Cabins / Yurts
- ❑ Day Use Area
- ❑

Notes:

Get the Facts

- ❑ Phone   (315) 783-1963
- ❑ Park Hours

    _____

- ❑ Reservations? _____Y _____N

    date made_____

- ❑ Open all year _____Y_____N

    dates_____

- ❑ Check in time _____
- ❑ Check out time _____
- ❑ Pet friendly _____Y _____N
- ❑ Max RV length _____
- ❑ Distance from home

    miles: _____

    hours: _____

- ❑ Address_____

    _____

    _____

Fees:

- ❑ Day Use $ _____
- ❑ Camp Sites $ _____
- ❑ RV Sites $ _____
- ❑ Refund policy

    _____

    _____

    _____

Make It Personal

Trip dates:
_____

The weather was: Sunny Cloudy Rainy Stormy Snowy Foggy Warm Cold

Why I went:
_____

_____

How I got there: (circle all that apply)   Plane   Train   Car   Bus   Bike   Hike   RV   MC
_____

I went with:
_____

We stayed in (space, cabin # etc):
_____

Most relaxing day:
_____

_____

Something funny:
_____

_____

Someone we met:
_____

_____

Best story told:
_____

_____

The kids liked this:
_____

_____

The best food:
_____

_____

Games played:
_____

_____

Something disappointing:
_____

_____

Next time I'll do this differently:
_____

_____

Robert Moses State Park - Thousand Islands

City: Massena   County: St. Lawrence

Plan your trip: https://parks.ny.gov/parks/robertmosesthousandislands/details.aspx

Activities:

- ❏ Biking
- ❏ Boating
- ❏ Canoeing
- ❏ Disc Golf
- ❏ Fishing / Ice
- ❏ Hiking
- ❏ Horseback Riding
- ❏ Hunting
- ❏ Kayaking
- ❏ Marina
- ❏ Nature Center / Trails

- ❏ Photography
- ❏ Playing Fields
- ❏ Scenic Views
- ❏ Swimming
- ❏ Waterfalls
- ❏ Wildlife & Birding
- ❏ Winter Sports
- ❏
- ❏
- ❏
- ❏

Facilities:

- ❏ ADA
- ❏ Picnic sites
- ❏ Restrooms
- ❏ Showers
- ❏ Trailer Access
- ❏ Visitor center

- ❏ Group Camping
- ❏ RV Camp
- ❏ Rustic Camping
- ❏ Cabins / Yurts
- ❏ Day Use Area
- ❏

Notes:

Get the Facts

- ❏ Phone   (315) 769-8663
- ❏ Park Hours

  _____

- ❏ Reservations? ____Y ____N

  date made_____

- ❏ Open all year ____Y____N

  dates_____

- ❏ Check in time _____
- ❏ Check out time _____
- ❏ Pet friendly _____Y _____N
- ❏ Max RV length _____
- ❏ Distance from home

  miles: _____

  hours: _____

- ❏ Address_____

  _____

  _____

Fees:

- ❏ Day Use $ _____
- ❏ Camp Sites $ _____
- ❏ RV Sites $ _____
- ❏ Refund policy

  _____

  _____

  _____

Make It Personal

Trip dates: _____ | The weather was: Sunny Cloudy Rainy Stormy Snowy Foggy Warm Cold

Why I went:
_____

_____

How I got there: (circle all that apply)   Plane   Train   Car   Bus   Bike   Hike   RV   MC
_____

I went with:
_____

We stayed in (space, cabin # etc):
_____

Most relaxing day:
_____

_____

Something funny:
_____

_____

Someone we met:
_____

_____

Best story told:
_____

_____

The kids liked this:
_____

_____

The best food:
_____

_____

Games played:
_____

_____

Something disappointing:
_____

_____

Next time I'll do this differently:
_____

_____

Jacques Cartier State Park
City: Morristown   County: St. Lawrence

Plan your trip: https://parks.ny.gov/parks/jacquescartier/details.aspx

Activities:

- ☐ Biking
- ☐ Boating
- ☐ Canoeing
- ☐ Disc Golf
- ☐ Fishing / Ice
- ☐ Hiking
- ☐ Horseback Riding
- ☐ Hunting
- ☐ Kayaking
- ☐ Marina
- ☐ Nature Center / Trails
- ☐ Photography
- ☐ Playing Fields
- ☐ Scenic Views
- ☐ Swimming
- ☐ Waterfalls
- ☐ Wildlife & Birding
- ☐ Winter Sports
- ☐
- ☐
- ☐
- ☐

Facilities:

- ☐ ADA
- ☐ Picnic sites
- ☐ Restrooms
- ☐ Showers
- ☐ Trailer Access
- ☐ Visitor center
- ☐ Group Camping
- ☐ RV Camp
- ☐ Rustic Camping
- ☐ Cabins / Yurts
- ☐ Day Use Area
- ☐

Notes:

Get the Facts

- ☐ Phone   (315) 375-6371
- ☐ Park Hours

_____

- ☐ Reservations? ____Y ____N

date made_____

- ☐ Open all year ____Y_____N

dates_____

- ☐ Check in time _____
- ☐ Check out time _____
- ☐ Pet friendly _____Y _____N
- ☐ Max RV length _____
- ☐ Distance from home

miles: _____

hours: _____

- ☐ Address_____

_____

_____

Fees:

- ☐ Day Use $ _____
- ☐ Camp Sites $ _____
- ☐ RV Sites $ _____
- ☐ Refund policy

_____

_____

_____

Make It Personal

Trip dates: _____

The weather was: Sunny Cloudy Rainy Stormy Snowy Foggy Warm Cold

Why I went:
_____

How I got there: (circle all that apply) Plane Train Car Bus Bike Hike RV MC

I went with:
_____

We stayed in (space, cabin # etc):
_____

Most relaxing day:
_____

Something funny:
_____

Someone we met:
_____

Best story told:
_____

The kids liked this:
_____

The best food:
_____

Games played:
_____

Something disappointing:
_____

Next time I'll do this differently:
_____
_____

Eel Weir State Park
City: Ogdensburg   County: St. Lawrence

Plan your trip: https://parks.ny.gov/parks/eelweir/details.aspx

Activities:

- ❏ Biking
- ❏ Boating
- ❏ Canoeing
- ❏ Disc Golf
- ❏ Fishing / Ice
- ❏ Hiking
- ❏ Horseback Riding
- ❏ Hunting
- ❏ Kayaking
- ❏ Marina
- ❏ Nature Center / Trails

- ❏ Photography
- ❏ Playing Fields
- ❏ Scenic Views
- ❏ Swimming
- ❏ Waterfalls
- ❏ Wildlife & Birding
- ❏ Winter Sports
- ❏
- ❏
- ❏
- ❏

Facilities:

- ❏ ADA
- ❏ Picnic sites
- ❏ Restrooms
- ❏ Showers
- ❏ Trailer Access
- ❏ Visitor center

- ❏ Group Camping
- ❏ RV Camp
- ❏ Rustic Camping
- ❏ Cabins / Yurts
- ❏ Day Use Area
- ❏

Notes:

Get the Facts

- ❏ Phone   (315) 393-1138
- ❏ Park Hours

  _____

- ❏ Reservations? ____Y ____N

  date made_____

- ❏ Open all year ____Y _____N

  dates_____

- ❏ Check in time _____
- ❏ Check out time _____
- ❏ Pet friendly _____Y _____N
- ❏ Max RV length _____
- ❏ Distance from home

  miles: _____

  hours: _____

- ❏ Address_____

  _____

  _____

Fees:

- ❏ Day Use $ _____
- ❏ Camp Sites $ _____
- ❏ RV Sites $ _____
- ❏ Refund policy

  _____

  _____

  _____

Make It Personal

Trip dates: _____ | The weather was: Sunny Cloudy Rainy Stormy Snowy Foggy Warm Cold

Why I went: _____

_____

How I got there: (circle all that apply) Plane Train Car Bus Bike Hike RV MC
_____

I went with: _____

We stayed in (space, cabin # etc): _____

Most relaxing day: _____

_____

Something funny: _____

_____

Someone we met: _____

_____

Best story told: _____

_____

The kids liked this: _____

_____

The best food: _____

_____

Games played: _____

_____

Something disappointing: _____

_____

Next time I'll do this differently: _____

_____

Coles Creek State Park
City: Waddington   County: St. Lawrence

Plan your trip: https://parks.ny.gov/parks/colescreek/details.aspx

Activities:

- ☐ Biking
- ☐ Boating
- ☐ Canoeing
- ☐ Disc Golf
- ☐ Fishing / Ice
- ☐ Hiking
- ☐ Horseback Riding
- ☐ Hunting
- ☐ Kayaking
- ☐ Marina
- ☐ Nature Center / Trails

- ☐ Photography
- ☐ Playing Fields
- ☐ Scenic Views
- ☐ Swimming
- ☐ Waterfalls
- ☐ Wildlife & Birding
- ☐ Winter Sports
- ☐
- ☐
- ☐
- ☐

Facilities:

- ☐ ADA
- ☐ Picnic sites
- ☐ Restrooms
- ☐ Showers
- ☐ Trailer Access
- ☐ Visitor center

- ☐ Group Camping
- ☐ RV Camp
- ☐ Rustic Camping
- ☐ Cabins / Yurts
- ☐ Day Use Area
- ☐

Notes:

Get the Facts

- ☐ Phone   (315) 388-5636
- ☐ Park Hours

_____

- ☐ Reservations? ____Y ____N

date made_____

- ☐ Open all year ____Y____N

dates_____

- ☐ Check in time _____
- ☐ Check out time _____
- ☐ Pet friendly _____Y _____N
- ☐ Max RV length _____
- ☐ Distance from home

miles: _____

hours: _____

- ☐ Address_____

_____

_____

Fees:

- ☐ Day Use $ _____
- ☐ Camp Sites $ _____
- ☐ RV Sites $ _____
- ☐ Refund policy

_____

_____

_____

Make It Personal

Trip dates:

The weather was: Sunny Cloudy Rainy Stormy Snowy Foggy Warm Cold

Why I went:

How I got there: (circle all that apply) Plane Train Car Bus Bike Hike RV MC

I went with:

We stayed in (space, cabin # etc):

Most relaxing day:

Something funny:

Someone we met:

Best story told:

The kids liked this:

The best food:

Games played:

Something disappointing:

Next time I'll do this differently:

Point Au Roche State Park
City: Fineview   County: Jefferson

Plan your trip: https://parks.ny.gov/parks/watersonpoint/details.aspx

Activities: (check all that apply)

- ❑ Beach
- ❑ Biking
- ❑ Boating
- ❑ Canoeing
- ❑ Fishing / Ice
- ❑ Hiking
- ❑ Horseback Riding
- ❑ Hunting
- ❑ Kayaking

- ❑ Marina
- ❑ Nature Center
- ❑ Photography
- ❑ Swimming
- ❑ Waterfalls
- ❑ Watersports
- ❑ Wildlife & Birding
- ❑ Winter Sports
- ❑

Facilities:

- ❑ ADA
- ❑ Gift Shop
- ❑ Museum
- ❑ Visitor Center
- ❑ Restrooms

- ❑ Playground
- ❑ Picnic sites
- ❑
- ❑
- ❑

Memories of the Trip

Get the Facts

- ❑ Phone   (315) 482-2722
- ❑ Park Hours

  _____

- ❑ Reservations? _____Y _____N

  date made_____

- ❑ Open all year? _____Y_____N

  dates_____

- ❑ Dog friendly _____Y _____N

- ❑ Distance from home

  miles: _____

  hours: _____

- ❑ Address_____

  _____

  _____

Fees:

- ❑ Day Use $ _____
- ❑ Refund policy

  _____

  _____

  _____

Stamps & Stickers

Waterson Point State Park
City: Plattsburgh   County: Jefferson

Plan your trip: https://parks.ny.gov/parks/watersonpoint/details.aspx

Activities: (check all that apply)

- ❑ Beach
- ❑ Biking
- ❑ Boating
- ❑ Canoeing
- ❑ Fishing / Ice
- ❑ Hiking
- ❑ Horseback Riding
- ❑ Hunting
- ❑ Kayaking

- ❑ Marina
- ❑ Nature Center
- ❑ Photography
- ❑ Swimming
- ❑ Waterfalls
- ❑ Watersports
- ❑ Wildlife & Birding
- ❑ Winter Sports
- ❑

Facilities:

- ❑ ADA
- ❑ Gift Shop
- ❑ Museum
- ❑ Visitor Center
- ❑ Restrooms

- ❑ Playground
- ❑ Picnic sites
- ❑
- ❑
- ❑

Memories of the Trip

Get the Facts

- ❑ Phone   (518) 563-0369
- ❑ Park Hours

  _____

- ❑ Reservations? _____ Y _____ N

  date made_____

- ❑ Open all year? _____ Y _____ N

  dates_____

- ❑ Dog friendly _____ Y _____ N

- ❑ Distance from home

  miles: _____

  hours: _____

- ❑ Address_____

  _____

  _____

Fees:

- ❑ Day Use $ _____
- ❑ Refund policy

  _____

  _____

  _____

Stamps & Stickers

Rock Island Lighthouse State Park
City: Fisher's Landing   County: Jefferson

Plan your trip: https://parks.ny.gov/parks/rockislandlighthouse/details.aspx

Activities: (check all that apply)

- ❑ Beach
- ❑ Biking
- ❑ Boating
- ❑ Canoeing
- ❑ Fishing / Ice
- ❑ Hiking
- ❑ Horseback Riding
- ❑ Hunting
- ❑ Kayaking

- ❑ Marina
- ❑ Nature Center
- ❑ Photography
- ❑ Swimming
- ❑ Waterfalls
- ❑ Watersports
- ❑ Wildlife & Birding
- ❑ Winter Sports
- ❑

Facilities:

- ❑ ADA
- ❑ Gift Shop
- ❑ Museum
- ❑ Visitor Center
- ❑ Restrooms

- ❑ Playground
- ❑ Picnic sites
- ❑
- ❑
- ❑

Get the Facts

- ❑ Phone   (315) 775-6886
- ❑ Park Hours

_____

- ❑ Reservations? ____Y ____N

date made_____

- ❑ Open all year? ____Y____N

dates_____

- ❑ Dog friendly _____Y _____N
- ❑ Distance from home

miles: _____

hours: _____

- ❑ Address_____

_____

_____

Fees:

- ❑ Day Use $ _____
- ❑ Refund policy

_____

_____

_____

Stamps & Stickers

Memories of the Trip

Niagara Region

- Niagara County
- Erie County

Golden Hill State Park

City: Barker   **County: Niagara**

Plan your trip: https://parks.ny.gov/parks/goldenhill/details.aspx

Activities:

- ❑ Biking
- ❑ Boating
- ❑ Canoeing
- ❑ Disc Golf
- ❑ Fishing / Ice
- ❑ Hiking
- ❑ Horseback Riding
- ❑ Hunting
- ❑ Kayaking
- ❑ Marina
- ❑ Nature Center / Trails

- ❑ Photography
- ❑ Playing Fields
- ❑ Scenic Views
- ❑ Swimming
- ❑ Waterfalls
- ❑ Wildlife & Birding
- ❑ Winter Sports
- ❑
- ❑
- ❑
- ❑

Facilities:

- ❑ ADA
- ❑ Picnic sites
- ❑ Restrooms
- ❑ Showers
- ❑ Trailer Access
- ❑ Visitor center

- ❑ Group Camping
- ❑ RV Camp
- ❑ Rustic Camping
- ❑ Cabins / Yurts
- ❑ Day Use Area
- ❑

Notes:

Get the Facts

- ❑ Phone   (716) 795-3885
- ❑ Park Hours

  _____

- ❑ Reservations? ____Y ____N

  date made_____

- ❑ Open all year ____Y____N

  dates_____

- ❑ Check in time _____
- ❑ Check out time _____
- ❑ Pet friendly _____Y _____N
- ❑ Max RV length _____
- ❑ Distance from home

  miles: _____

  hours: _____

- ❑ Address_____

  _____

  _____

Fees:

- ❑ Day Use $ _____
- ❑ Camp Sites $ _____
- ❑ RV Sites $ _____
- ❑ Refund policy

  _____

  _____

  _____

Make It Personal

Trip dates: _____ | The weather was: Sunny Cloudy Rainy Stormy Snowy Foggy Warm Cold

Why I went:
_____
_____

How I got there: (circle all that apply)   Plane   Train   Car   Bus   Bike   Hike   RV   MC
_____

I went with:
_____

We stayed in (space, cabin # etc):
_____

Most relaxing day:
_____
_____

Something funny:
_____
_____

Someone we met:
_____
_____

Best story told:
_____
_____

The kids liked this:
_____
_____

The best food:
_____
_____

Games played:
_____
_____

Something disappointing:
_____
_____

Next time I'll do this differently:
_____
_____

Four Mile Creek State Park
City: Youngstown   County: Niagara

Plan your trip: https://parks.ny.gov/parks/fourmile/details.aspx

Activities:

- ❑ Biking
- ❑ Boating
- ❑ Canoeing
- ❑ Disc Golf
- ❑ Fishing / Ice
- ❑ Hiking
- ❑ Horseback Riding
- ❑ Hunting
- ❑ Kayaking
- ❑ Marina
- ❑ Nature Center / Trails

- ❑ Photography
- ❑ Playing Fields
- ❑ Scenic Views
- ❑ Swimming
- ❑ Waterfalls
- ❑ Wildlife & Birding
- ❑ Winter Sports
- ❑
- ❑
- ❑
- ❑

Facilities:

- ❑ ADA
- ❑ Picnic sites
- ❑ Restrooms
- ❑ Showers
- ❑ Trailer Access
- ❑ Visitor center

- ❑ Group Camping
- ❑ RV Camp
- ❑ Rustic Camping
- ❑ Cabins / Yurts
- ❑ Day Use Area
- ❑

Notes:

Get the Facts

- ❑ Phone   (716) 745-3802
- ❑ Park Hours

  _____

- ❑ Reservations? _____Y _____N

  date made_____

- ❑ Open all year _____Y_____N

  dates_____

- ❑ Check in time _____
- ❑ Check out time _____
- ❑ Pet friendly _____Y _____N
- ❑ Max RV length _____
- ❑ Distance from home

  miles: _____

  hours: _____

- ❑ Address_____

  _____

  _____

Fees:

- ❑ Day Use $ _____
- ❑ Camp Sites $ _____
- ❑ RV Sites $ _____
- ❑ Refund policy

  _____

  _____

  _____

Make It Personal

Trip dates: _____ | The weather was: Sunny Cloudy Rainy Stormy Snowy Foggy Warm Cold

Why I went: _____

_____

How I got there: (circle all that apply)   Plane   Train   Car   Bus   Bike   Hike   RV   MC

I went with: _____

We stayed in (space, cabin # etc): _____

Most relaxing day: _____

_____

Something funny: _____

_____

Someone we met: _____

_____

Best story told: _____

_____

The kids liked this: _____

_____

The best food: _____

_____

Games played: _____

_____

Something disappointing: _____

_____

Next time I'll do this differently: _____

_____

Woodlawn Beach State Park
City: Blasdell   County: Erie

Plan your trip: https://parks.ny.gov/parks/woodlawnbeach/details.aspx

Activities: (check all that apply)

- ❑ Beach
- ❑ Biking
- ❑ Boating
- ❑ Canoeing
- ❑ Fishing / Ice
- ❑ Hiking
- ❑ Horseback Riding
- ❑ Hunting
- ❑ Kayaking

- ❑ Marina
- ❑ Nature Center
- ❑ Photography
- ❑ Swimming
- ❑ Waterfalls
- ❑ Watersports
- ❑ Wildlife & Birding
- ❑ Winter Sports
- ❑

Facilities:

- ❑ ADA
- ❑ Gift Shop
- ❑ Museum
- ❑ Visitor Center
- ❑ Restrooms

- ❑ Playground
- ❑ Picnic sites
- ❑
- ❑
- ❑

Memories of the Trip

Get the Facts

- ❑ Phone   (716) 826-1930
- ❑ Park Hours

_____

- ❑ Reservations? ____Y ____N

date made_____

- ❑ Open all year? ____Y____N

dates_____

- ❑ Dog friendly _____Y _____N
- ❑ Distance from home

miles: _____

hours: _____

- ❑ Address_____

_____

_____

Fees:

- ❑ Day Use $ _____
- ❑ Refund policy

_____

_____

_____

Stamps & Stickers

Buffalo Harbor State Park
City: Buffalo   County: Erie

Plan your trip: https://parks.ny.gov/parks/buffaloharbor/details.aspx

Activities: (check all that apply)

- ❑ Beach
- ❑ Biking
- ❑ Boating
- ❑ Canoeing
- ❑ Fishing / Ice
- ❑ Hiking
- ❑ Horseback Riding
- ❑ Hunting
- ❑ Kayaking

- ❑ Marina
- ❑ Nature Center
- ❑ Photography
- ❑ Swimming
- ❑ Waterfalls
- ❑ Watersports
- ❑ Wildlife & Birding
- ❑ Winter Sports
- ❑

Facilities:

- ❑ ADA
- ❑ Gift Shop
- ❑ Museum
- ❑ Visitor Center
- ❑ Restrooms

- ❑ Playground
- ❑ Picnic sites
- ❑
- ❑
- ❑

Memories of the Trip

Get the Facts

- ❑ Phone   (716) 822-1207
- ❑ Park Hours

  _____

- ❑ Reservations? ____Y ____N

  date made_____

- ❑ Open all year? ____Y____N

  dates_____

- ❑ Dog friendly _____Y _____N
- ❑ Distance from home

  miles: _____

  hours: _____

- ❑ Address_____

  _____

  _____

Fees:

- ❑ Day Use $ _____
- ❑ Refund policy

  _____

  _____

  _____

Stamps & Stickers

Knox Farm State Park
City: East Aurora   County: Erie

Plan your trip: https://parks.ny.gov/parks/knoxfarm/details.aspx

Activities: (check all that apply)

- ❑ Beach
- ❑ Biking
- ❑ Boating
- ❑ Canoeing
- ❑ Fishing / Ice
- ❑ Hiking
- ❑ Horseback Riding
- ❑ Hunting
- ❑ Kayaking

- ❑ Marina
- ❑ Nature Center
- ❑ Photography
- ❑ Swimming
- ❑ Waterfalls
- ❑ Watersports
- ❑ Wildlife & Birding
- ❑ Winter Sports
- ❑

Facilities:

- ❑ ADA
- ❑ Gift Shop
- ❑ Museum
- ❑ Visitor Center
- ❑ Restrooms

- ❑ Playground
- ❑ Picnic sites
- ❑
- ❑
- ❑

Memories of the Trip

Get the Facts

- ❑ Phone   (716) 652-0786
- ❑ Park Hours

_____

- ❑ Reservations? ____ Y ____ N

date made_____

- ❑ Open all year? ____ Y ____ N

dates_____

- ❑ Dog friendly ____ Y ____ N
- ❑ Distance from home

miles: _____

hours: _____

- ❑ Address_____

_____

_____

Fees:

- ❑ Day Use $ _____
- ❑ Refund policy

_____

_____

_____

Stamps & Stickers

Beaver Island State Park
City: Grand Island   County: Erie

Plan your trip: https://parks.ny.gov/parks/beaverisland/details.aspx

Activities: (check all that apply)

- ❏ Beach
- ❏ Biking
- ❏ Boating
- ❏ Canoeing
- ❏ Fishing / Ice
- ❏ Hiking
- ❏ Horseback Riding
- ❏ Hunting
- ❏ Kayaking

- ❏ Marina
- ❏ Nature Center
- ❏ Photography
- ❏ Swimming
- ❏ Waterfalls
- ❏ Watersports
- ❏ Wildlife & Birding
- ❏ Winter Sports
- ❏

Facilities:

- ❏ ADA
- ❏ Gift Shop
- ❏ Museum
- ❏ Visitor Center
- ❏ Restrooms

- ❏ Playground
- ❏ Picnic sites
- ❏
- ❏
- ❏

Memories of the Trip

Get the Facts

- ❏ Phone   (716) 404-4214
- ❏ Park Hours

  _____

- ❏ Reservations? _____Y _____N

  date made_____

- ❏ Open all year? _____Y_____N

  dates_____

- ❏ Dog friendly _____Y _____N
- ❏ Distance from home

  miles: _____

  hours: _____

- ❏ Address_____

  _____

  _____

Fees:

- ❏ Day Use $ _____
- ❏ Refund policy

  _____

  _____

  _____

Stamps & Stickers

Buckhorn Island State Park
City: Grand Island   County: Erie

Plan your trip: https://parks.ny.gov/parks/buckhornisland/details.aspx

Activities: (check all that apply)

- ❑ Beach
- ❑ Biking
- ❑ Boating
- ❑ Canoeing
- ❑ Fishing / Ice
- ❑ Hiking
- ❑ Horseback Riding
- ❑ Hunting
- ❑ Kayaking

- ❑ Marina
- ❑ Nature Center
- ❑ Photography
- ❑ Swimming
- ❑ Waterfalls
- ❑ Watersports
- ❑ Wildlife & Birding
- ❑ Winter Sports
- ❑

Facilities:

- ❑ ADA
- ❑ Gift Shop
- ❑ Museum
- ❑ Visitor Center
- ❑ Restrooms

- ❑ Playground
- ❑ Picnic sites
- ❑
- ❑
- ❑

Memories of the Trip

Get the Facts

- ❑ Phone   (716) 773-3271
- ❑ Park Hours

_____

- ❑ Reservations? _____ Y _____ N

date made_____

- ❑ Open all year? _____ Y _____ N

dates_____

- ❑ Dog friendly _____ Y _____ N
- ❑ Distance from home

miles: _____

hours: _____

- ❑ Address_____

_____

_____

Fees:

- ❑ Day Use $ _____
- ❑ Refund policy

_____

_____

_____

Stamps & Stickers

Artpark State Park (Earl W. Brydges)
City: Lewiston   County: Niagara
Plan your trip: https://parks.ny.gov/parks/artpark/details.aspx

Activities: (check all that apply)

- ❑ Beach
- ❑ Biking
- ❑ Boating
- ❑ Canoeing
- ❑ Fishing / Ice
- ❑ Hiking
- ❑ Horseback Riding
- ❑ Hunting
- ❑ Kayaking

- ❑ Marina
- ❑ Nature Center
- ❑ Photography
- ❑ Swimming
- ❑ Waterfalls
- ❑ Watersports
- ❑ Wildlife & Birding
- ❑ Winter Sports
- ❑

Facilities:

- ❑ ADA
- ❑ Gift Shop
- ❑ Museum
- ❑ Visitor Center
- ❑ Restrooms

- ❑ Playground
- ❑ Picnic sites
- ❑
- ❑
- ❑

Memories of the Trip

Get the Facts

- ❑ Phone   (716) 754-7766
- ❑ Park Hours

  _____

- ❑ Reservations? ____Y ____N

  date made_____
- ❑ Open all year? ____Y____N

  dates_____
- ❑ Dog friendly _____Y _____N
- ❑ Distance from home

  miles: _____

  hours: _____
- ❑ Address_____

  _____

  _____

Fees:

- ❑ Day Use $ _____
- ❑ Refund policy

  _____

  _____

  _____

Stamps & Stickers

Joseph Davis State Park
City: Lewiston   County: Niagara

Plan your trip: https://parks.ny.gov/parks/josephdavis/details.aspx

Activities: (check all that apply)

- ❑ Beach
- ❑ Biking
- ❑ Boating
- ❑ Canoeing
- ❑ Fishing / Ice
- ❑ Hiking
- ❑ Horseback Riding
- ❑ Hunting
- ❑ Kayaking

- ❑ Marina
- ❑ Nature Center
- ❑ Photography
- ❑ Swimming
- ❑ Waterfalls
- ❑ Watersports
- ❑ Wildlife & Birding
- ❑ Winter Sports
- ❑

Facilities:

- ❑ ADA
- ❑ Gift Shop
- ❑ Museum
- ❑ Visitor Center
- ❑ Restrooms

- ❑ Playground
- ❑ Picnic sites
- ❑
- ❑
- ❑

Memories of the Trip

Get the Facts

- ❑ Phone   (716) 745-7273
- ❑ Park Hours

    _____

- ❑ Reservations? ____Y ____N

date made_____

- ❑ Open all year? ____Y____N

dates_____

- ❑ Dog friendly _____Y _____N
- ❑ Distance from home

miles: _____

hours: _____

- ❑ Address_____

_____

_____

Fees:

- ❑ Day Use $ _____
- ❑ Refund policy

_____

_____

_____

Stamps & Stickers

DeVeaux Woods State Park
City: Niagara Falls   County: Niagara

Plan your trip: https://parks.ny.gov/parks/deveauxwoods/details.aspx

Activities: (check all that apply)

- ❑ Beach
- ❑ Biking
- ❑ Boating
- ❑ Canoeing
- ❑ Fishing / Ice
- ❑ Hiking
- ❑ Horseback Riding
- ❑ Hunting
- ❑ Kayaking

- ❑ Marina
- ❑ Nature Center
- ❑ Photography
- ❑ Swimming
- ❑ Waterfalls
- ❑ Watersports
- ❑ Wildlife & Birding
- ❑ Winter Sports
- ❑

Facilities:

- ❑ ADA
- ❑ Gift Shop
- ❑ Museum
- ❑ Visitor Center
- ❑ Restrooms

- ❑ Playground
- ❑ Picnic sites
- ❑
- ❑
- ❑

Memories of the Trip

Get the Facts

- ❑ Phone   (716) 284-5778
- ❑ Park Hours

  _____

- ❑ Reservations? ____Y ____N

  date made_____

- ❑ Open all year? ____Y____N

  dates_____

- ❑ Dog friendly _____Y _____N
- ❑ Distance from home

  miles: _____

  hours: _____

- ❑ Address_____

  _____

  _____

Fees:

- ❑ Day Use $ _____
- ❑ Refund policy

  _____

  _____

  _____

Stamps & Stickers

Devil's Hole State Park

City: Niagara Falls   County: Niagara

Plan your trip: https://parks.ny.gov/parks/devilshole/details.aspx

Activities: (check all that apply)

- ❑ Beach
- ❑ Biking
- ❑ Boating
- ❑ Canoeing
- ❑ Fishing / Ice
- ❑ Hiking
- ❑ Horseback Riding
- ❑ Hunting
- ❑ Kayaking

- ❑ Marina
- ❑ Nature Center
- ❑ Photography
- ❑ Swimming
- ❑ Waterfalls
- ❑ Watersports
- ❑ Wildlife & Birding
- ❑ Winter Sports
- ❑

Facilities:

- ❑ ADA
- ❑ Gift Shop
- ❑ Museum
- ❑ Visitor Center
- ❑ Restrooms

- ❑ Playground
- ❑ Picnic sites
- ❑
- ❑
- ❑

Memories of the Trip

Get the Facts

- ❑ Phone   (716) 284-5778
- ❑ Park Hours

  _____

- ❑ Reservations? ____Y ____N

  date made_____

- ❑ Open all year? ____Y____N

  dates_____

- ❑ Dog friendly _____Y _____N

- ❑ Distance from home

  miles: _____

  hours: _____

- ❑ Address_____

  _____

  _____

Fees:

- ❑ Day Use $ _____
- ❑ Refund policy

  _____

  _____

  _____

Stamps & Stickers

Niagara Falls State Park
City: Niagara Falls   County: Niagara

Plan your trip: https://parks.ny.gov/parks/niagarafallsusa/details.aspx

Activities: (check all that apply)

- ❑ Beach
- ❑ Biking
- ❑ Boating
- ❑ Canoeing
- ❑ Fishing / Ice
- ❑ Hiking
- ❑ Horseback Riding
- ❑ Hunting
- ❑ Kayaking

- ❑ Marina
- ❑ Nature Center
- ❑ Photography
- ❑ Swimming
- ❑ Waterfalls
- ❑ Watersports
- ❑ Wildlife & Birding
- ❑ Winter Sports
- ❑

Facilities:

- ❑ ADA
- ❑ Gift Shop
- ❑ Museum
- ❑ Visitor Center
- ❑ Restrooms

- ❑ Playground
- ❑ Picnic sites
- ❑
- ❑
- ❑

Memories of the Trip

Get the Facts

- ❑ Phone   (716) 278-1794
- ❑ Park Hours

  _____

- ❑ Reservations? ____Y ____N

  date made_____

- ❑ Open all year? ____Y____N

  dates_____

- ❑ Dog friendly _____Y _____N

- ❑ Distance from home

  miles: _____

  hours: _____

- ❑ Address_____

  _____

  _____

Fees:

- ❑ Day Use $ _____
- ❑ Refund policy

  _____

  _____

  _____

Stamps & Stickers

Reservoir State Park
City: Niagara Falls   County: Niagara

Plan your trip: https://parks.ny.gov/parks/reservoir/details.aspx

Activities: (check all that apply)

- ❑ Beach
- ❑ Biking
- ❑ Boating
- ❑ Canoeing
- ❑ Fishing / Ice
- ❑ Hiking
- ❑ Horseback Riding
- ❑ Hunting
- ❑ Kayaking
- ❑ Marina
- ❑ Nature Center
- ❑ Photography
- ❑ Swimming
- ❑ Waterfalls
- ❑ Watersports
- ❑ Wildlife & Birding
- ❑ Winter Sports
- ❑

Facilities:

- ❑ ADA
- ❑ Gift Shop
- ❑ Museum
- ❑ Visitor Center
- ❑ Restrooms
- ❑ Playground
- ❑ Picnic sites
- ❑
- ❑
- ❑

Memories of the Trip

Get the Facts

- ❑ Phone   (716) 284-5778
- ❑ Park Hours

  _____

- ❑ Reservations? _____ Y _____ N

  date made_____

- ❑ Open all year? _____ Y_____ N

  dates_____

- ❑ Dog friendly _____ Y _____ N
- ❑ Distance from home

  miles: _____

  hours: _____

- ❑ Address_____

  _____

  _____

Fees:

- ❑ Day Use $ _____
- ❑ Refund policy

  _____

  _____

  _____

Stamps & Stickers

Whirlpool State Park

City: Niagara Falls   County: Niagara

Plan your trip: https://parks.ny.gov/parks/whirlpool/details.aspx

Activities: (check all that apply)

- ❑ Beach
- ❑ Biking
- ❑ Boating
- ❑ Canoeing
- ❑ Fishing / Ice
- ❑ Hiking
- ❑ Horseback Riding
- ❑ Hunting
- ❑ Kayaking

- ❑ Marina
- ❑ Nature Center
- ❑ Photography
- ❑ Swimming
- ❑ Waterfalls
- ❑ Watersports
- ❑ Wildlife & Birding
- ❑ Winter Sports
- ❑

Facilities:

- ❑ ADA
- ❑ Gift Shop
- ❑ Museum
- ❑ Visitor Center
- ❑ Restrooms

- ❑ Playground
- ❑ Picnic sites
- ❑
- ❑
- ❑

Memories of the Trip

Get the Facts

- ❑ Phone   (716) 284-4691
- ❑ Park Hours

  _____

- ❑ Reservations? _____Y _____N

  date made_____

- ❑ Open all year? _____Y_____N

  dates_____

- ❑ Dog friendly _____Y _____N
- ❑ Distance from home

  miles: _____

  hours: _____

- ❑ Address_____

  _____

  _____

Fees:

- ❑ Day Use $ _____
- ❑ Refund policy

  _____

  _____

  _____

Stamps & Stickers

Wilson-Tuscarora State Park
City: Wilson   County: Niagara

Plan your trip: https://parks.ny.gov/parks/wilsontuscarora/details.aspx

Activities: (check all that apply)

- ❑ Beach
- ❑ Biking
- ❑ Boating
- ❑ Canoeing
- ❑ Fishing / Ice
- ❑ Hiking
- ❑ Horseback Riding
- ❑ Hunting
- ❑ Kayaking

- ❑ Marina
- ❑ Nature Center
- ❑ Photography
- ❑ Swimming
- ❑ Waterfalls
- ❑ Watersports
- ❑ Wildlife & Birding
- ❑ Winter Sports
- ❑

Facilities:

- ❑ ADA
- ❑ Gift Shop
- ❑ Museum
- ❑ Visitor Center
- ❑ Restrooms

- ❑ Playground
- ❑ Picnic sites
- ❑
- ❑
- ❑

Memories of the Trip

Get the Facts

- ❑ Phone   (716) 751-6361
- ❑ Park Hours

  _____

- ❑ Reservations? ____Y ____N

  date made_____

- ❑ Open all year? ____Y____N

  dates_____

- ❑ Dog friendly _____Y _____N

- ❑ Distance from home

  miles: _____

  hours: _____

- ❑ Address_____

  _____

  _____

Fees:

- ❑ Day Use $ _____
- ❑ Refund policy

  _____

  _____

  _____

Stamps & Stickers

Fort Niagara State Park
City: Youngstown　　　　　County: Niagara

Plan your trip: https://parks.ny.gov/parks/fortniagara/details.aspx

Activities: (check all that apply)

- ❑ Beach
- ❑ Biking
- ❑ Boating
- ❑ Canoeing
- ❑ Fishing / Ice
- ❑ Hiking
- ❑ Horseback Riding
- ❑ Hunting
- ❑ Kayaking

- ❑ Marina
- ❑ Nature Center
- ❑ Photography
- ❑ Swimming
- ❑ Waterfalls
- ❑ Watersports
- ❑ Wildlife & Birding
- ❑ Winter Sports
- ❑

Facilities:

- ❑ ADA
- ❑ Gift Shop
- ❑ Museum
- ❑ Visitor Center
- ❑ Restrooms

- ❑ Playground
- ❑ Picnic sites
- ❑
- ❑
- ❑

Memories of the Trip

Get the Facts

- ❑ Phone　(716) 745-7273
- ❑ Park Hours

_____

- ❑ Reservations? _____Y _____N

  date made_____

- ❑ Open all year? _____Y_____N

  dates_____

- ❑ Dog friendly _____Y _____N
- ❑ Distance from home

  miles: _____

  hours: _____

- ❑ Address_____

_____

_____

Fees:

- ❑ Day Use $ _____
- ❑ Refund policy

_____

_____

_____

Stamps & Stickers

Notes:

Genesee Region

- Genesee County
- Livingston County
- Monroe County
- Orleans County
- Wyoming County

Darien Lakes State Park
City: Darien Center   County: Genesee

Plan your trip: https://parks.ny.gov/parks/darienlakes/details.aspx

Activities:

- ❑ Biking
- ❑ Boating
- ❑ Canoeing
- ❑ Disc Golf
- ❑ Fishing / Ice
- ❑ Hiking
- ❑ Horseback Riding
- ❑ Hunting
- ❑ Kayaking
- ❑ Marina
- ❑ Nature Center / Trails

- ❑ Photography
- ❑ Playing Fields
- ❑ Scenic Views
- ❑ Swimming
- ❑ Waterfalls
- ❑ Wildlife & Birding
- ❑ Winter Sports
- ❑
- ❑
- ❑
- ❑

Facilities:

- ❑ ADA
- ❑ Picnic sites
- ❑ Restrooms
- ❑ Showers
- ❑ Trailer Access
- ❑ Visitor center

- ❑ Group Camping
- ❑ RV Camp
- ❑ Rustic Camping
- ❑ Cabins / Yurts
- ❑ Day Use Area
- ❑

Notes:

Get the Facts

- ❑ Phone   (585) 547-9242
- ❑ Park Hours

  _____
- ❑ Reservations? _____ Y _____ N

  date made_____
- ❑ Open all year _____ Y _____ N

  dates_____
- ❑ Check in time _____
- ❑ Check out time _____
- ❑ Pet friendly _____ Y _____ N
- ❑ Max RV length _____
- ❑ Distance from home

  miles: _____

  hours: _____
- ❑ Address_____

  _____

  _____

Fees:

- ❑ Day Use $ _____
- ❑ Camp Sites $ _____
- ❑ RV Sites $ _____
- ❑ Refund policy

  _____

  _____

  _____

Make It Personal

Trip dates: _____ | The weather was: Sunny Cloudy Rainy Stormy Snowy Foggy Warm Cold

Why I went:
_____

_____

How I got there: (circle all that apply)   Plane   Train   Car   Bus   Bike   Hike   RV   MC
_____

I went with:
_____

We stayed in (space, cabin # etc):
_____

Most relaxing day:
_____

_____

Something funny:
_____

_____

Someone we met:
_____

_____

Best story told:
_____

_____

The kids liked this:
_____

_____

The best food:
_____

_____

Games played:
_____

_____

Something disappointing:
_____

_____

Next time I'll do this differently:
_____

_____

Stony Brook State Park
City: Dansville   County: Livingston

Plan your trip: https://parks.ny.gov/parks/stonybrook/details.aspx

Activities:

- ❏ Biking
- ❏ Boating
- ❏ Canoeing
- ❏ Disc Golf
- ❏ Fishing / Ice
- ❏ Hiking
- ❏ Horseback Riding
- ❏ Hunting
- ❏ Kayaking
- ❏ Marina
- ❏ Nature Center / Trails

- ❏ Photography
- ❏ Playing Fields
- ❏ Scenic Views
- ❏ Swimming
- ❏ Waterfalls
- ❏ Wildlife & Birding
- ❏ Winter Sports
- ❏
- ❏
- ❏
- ❏

Facilities:

- ❏ ADA
- ❏ Picnic sites
- ❏ Restrooms
- ❏ Showers
- ❏ Trailer Access
- ❏ Visitor center

- ❏ Group Camping
- ❏ RV Camp
- ❏ Rustic Camping
- ❏ Cabins / Yurts
- ❏ Day Use Area
- ❏

Notes:

Get the Facts

- ❏ Phone   (585) 335-8111
- ❏ Park Hours

  _____

- ❏ Reservations? ____Y ____N

  date made_____

- ❏ Open all year ____Y_____N

  dates_____

- ❏ Check in time _____
- ❏ Check out time _____
- ❏ Pet friendly _____Y ____N
- ❏ Max RV length _____
- ❏ Distance from home

  miles: _____

  hours: _____

- ❏ Address_____

  _____

  _____

Fees:

- ❏ Day Use $ _____
- ❏ Camp Sites $ _____
- ❏ RV Sites $ _____
- ❏ Refund policy

  _____

  _____

  _____

Make It Personal

Trip dates: _____ | The weather was: Sunny Cloudy Rainy Stormy Snowy Foggy Warm Cold

Why I went: _____

_____

How I got there: (circle all that apply)   Plane   Train   Car   Bus   Bike   Hike   RV   MC

I went with: _____

We stayed in (space, cabin # etc): _____

Most relaxing day: _____

_____

Something funny: _____

_____

Someone we met: _____

_____

Best story told: _____

_____

The kids liked this: _____

_____

The best food: _____

_____

Games played: _____

_____

Something disappointing: _____

_____

Next time I'll do this differently: _____

_____

Hamlin Beach State Park
City: Hamlin
County: Monroe

Plan your trip: https://parks.ny.gov/parks/hamlinbeach/details.aspx

Activities:

- ❑ Biking
- ❑ Boating
- ❑ Canoeing
- ❑ Disc Golf
- ❑ Fishing / Ice
- ❑ Hiking
- ❑ Horseback Riding
- ❑ Hunting
- ❑ Kayaking
- ❑ Marina
- ❑ Nature Center / Trails

- ❑ Photography
- ❑ Playing Fields
- ❑ Scenic Views
- ❑ Swimming
- ❑ Waterfalls
- ❑ Wildlife & Birding
- ❑ Winter Sports
- ❑
- ❑
- ❑
- ❑

Facilities:

- ❑ ADA
- ❑ Picnic sites
- ❑ Restrooms
- ❑ Showers
- ❑ Trailer Access
- ❑ Visitor center

- ❑ Group Camping
- ❑ RV Camp
- ❑ Rustic Camping
- ❑ Cabins / Yurts
- ❑ Day Use Area
- ❑

Notes:

Get the Facts

- ❑ Phone   (585) 964-2462
- ❑ Park Hours

  _____

- ❑ Reservations? _____Y _____N

  date made_____

- ❑ Open all year _____Y_____N

  dates_____

- ❑ Check in time _____
- ❑ Check out time _____
- ❑ Pet friendly _____Y _____N
- ❑ Max RV length _____
- ❑ Distance from home

  miles: _____

  hours: _____

- ❑ Address_____

  _____

  _____

Fees:

- ❑ Day Use $ _____
- ❑ Camp Sites $ _____
- ❑ RV Sites $ _____
- ❑ Refund policy

  _____

  _____

  _____

Make It Personal

Trip dates: _____

The weather was: Sunny Cloudy Rainy Stormy Snowy Foggy Warm Cold

Why I went:
_____

How I got there: (circle all that apply) Plane Train Car Bus Bike Hike RV MC

I went with:
_____

We stayed in (space, cabin # etc):
_____

Most relaxing day:
_____

Something funny:
_____

Someone we met:
_____

Best story told:
_____

The kids liked this:
_____

The best food:
_____

Games played:
_____

Something disappointing:
_____

Next time I'll do this differently:
_____
_____

Lakeside Beach State Park
City: Waterport   County: Orleans

Plan your trip: https://parks.ny.gov/parks/lakesidebeach/details.aspx

Activities:

- ❑ Biking
- ❑ Boating
- ❑ Canoeing
- ❑ Disc Golf
- ❑ Fishing / Ice
- ❑ Hiking
- ❑ Horseback Riding
- ❑ Hunting
- ❑ Kayaking
- ❑ Marina
- ❑ Nature Center / Trails

- ❑ Photography
- ❑ Playing Fields
- ❑ Scenic Views
- ❑ Swimming
- ❑ Waterfalls
- ❑ Wildlife & Birding
- ❑ Winter Sports
- ❑
- ❑
- ❑
- ❑

Facilities:

- ❑ ADA
- ❑ Picnic sites
- ❑ Restrooms
- ❑ Showers
- ❑ Trailer Access
- ❑ Visitor center

- ❑ Group Camping
- ❑ RV Camp
- ❑ Rustic Camping
- ❑ Cabins / Yurts
- ❑ Day Use Area
- ❑

Notes:

Get the Facts

- ❑ Phone   (585) 682-4888
- ❑ Park Hours

  _____

- ❑ Reservations? ____Y ____N

  date made_____

- ❑ Open all year ____Y____N

  dates_____

- ❑ Check in time _____
- ❑ Check out time _____
- ❑ Pet friendly _____Y _____N
- ❑ Max RV length _____
- ❑ Distance from home

  miles: _____

  hours: _____

- ❑ Address_____

  _____

  _____

Fees:

- ❑ Day Use $ _____
- ❑ Camp Sites $ _____
- ❑ RV Sites $ _____
- ❑ Refund policy

  _____

  _____

  _____

Make It Personal

Trip dates: _____ | The weather was: Sunny Cloudy Rainy Stormy Snowy Foggy Warm Cold

Why I went: _____

_____

How I got there: (circle all that apply)   Plane   Train   Car   Bus   Bike   Hike   RV   MC

I went with: _____

We stayed in (space, cabin # etc): _____

Most relaxing day: _____

_____

Something funny: _____

_____

Someone we met: _____

_____

Best story told: _____

_____

The kids liked this: _____

_____

The best food: _____

_____

Games played: _____

_____

Something disappointing: _____

_____

Next time I'll do this differently: _____

_____

Letchworth State Park
City: Castile   County: Wyoming

Plan your trip: https://parks.ny.gov/parks/letchworth/details.aspx

Activities:

- ❏ Biking
- ❏ Boating
- ❏ Canoeing
- ❏ Disc Golf
- ❏ Fishing / Ice
- ❏ Hiking
- ❏ Horseback Riding
- ❏ Hunting
- ❏ Kayaking
- ❏ Marina
- ❏ Nature Center / Trails

- ❏ Photography
- ❏ Playing Fields
- ❏ Scenic Views
- ❏ Swimming
- ❏ Waterfalls
- ❏ Wildlife & Birding
- ❏ Winter Sports
- ❏
- ❏
- ❏
- ❏

Facilities:

- ❏ ADA
- ❏ Picnic sites
- ❏ Restrooms
- ❏ Showers
- ❏ Trailer Access
- ❏ Visitor center

- ❏ Group Camping
- ❏ RV Camp
- ❏ Rustic Camping
- ❏ Cabins / Yurts
- ❏ Day Use Area
- ❏

Notes:

Get the Facts

- ❏ Phone   (585) 493-3600
- ❏ Park Hours

  _____

- ❏ Reservations? ____Y ____N

  date made_____

- ❏ Open all year ____Y____N

  dates_____

- ❏ Check in time _____
- ❏ Check out time _____
- ❏ Pet friendly _____Y _____N
- ❏ Max RV length _____
- ❏ Distance from home

  miles: _____

  hours: _____

- ❏ Address_____

  _____

  _____

Fees:

- ❏ Day Use $ _____
- ❏ Camp Sites $ _____
- ❏ RV Sites $ _____
- ❏ Refund policy

  _____

  _____

  _____

Make It Personal

Trip dates: _____ | The weather was: Sunny Cloudy Rainy Stormy Snowy Foggy Warm Cold

Why I went:
_____

_____

How I got there: (circle all that apply) Plane Train Car Bus Bike Hike RV MC
_____

I went with:
_____

We stayed in (space, cabin # etc):
_____

Most relaxing day:
_____

_____

Something funny:
_____

_____

Someone we met:
_____

_____

Best story told:
_____

_____

The kids liked this:
_____

_____

The best food:
_____

_____

Games played:
_____

_____

Something disappointing:
_____

_____

Next time I'll do this differently:
_____

_____

Harrier Hollister Spencer State Recreation Area

City: Springwater   County: Livingston

Plan your trip: https://parks.ny.gov/parks/harriethollisterspencer/details.aspx

Activities: (check all that apply)

- ❑ Beach
- ❑ Biking
- ❑ Boating
- ❑ Canoeing
- ❑ Fishing / Ice
- ❑ Hiking
- ❑ Horseback Riding
- ❑ Hunting
- ❑ Kayaking

- ❑ Marina
- ❑ Nature Center
- ❑ Photography
- ❑ Swimming
- ❑ Waterfalls
- ❑ Watersports
- ❑ Wildlife & Birding
- ❑ Winter Sports
- ❑

Facilities:

- ❑ ADA
- ❑ Gift Shop
- ❑ Museum
- ❑ Visitor Center
- ❑ Restrooms

- ❑ Playground
- ❑ Picnic sites
- ❑
- ❑
- ❑

Memories of the Trip

Get the Facts

- ❑ Phone   (585) 335-8111
- ❑ Park Hours

  _____

- ❑ Reservations? _____Y _____N

  date made_____

- ❑ Open all year? _____Y_____N

  dates_____

- ❑ Dog friendly _____Y _____N

- ❑ Distance from home

  miles: _____

  hours: _____

- ❑ Address_____

  _____

  _____

Fees:

- ❑ Day Use $ _____
- ❑ Refund policy

  _____

  _____

  _____

Stamps & Stickers

Irondequoit Bay State Marine Park
City: Irondequoit   County: Monroe

Plan your trip: https://parks.ny.gov/parks/irondequoitbay/details.aspx

Activities: (check all that apply)

- ❑ Beach
- ❑ Biking
- ❑ Boating
- ❑ Canoeing
- ❑ Fishing / Ice
- ❑ Hiking
- ❑ Horseback Riding
- ❑ Hunting
- ❑ Kayaking

- ❑ Marina
- ❑ Nature Center
- ❑ Photography
- ❑ Swimming
- ❑ Waterfalls
- ❑ Watersports
- ❑ Wildlife & Birding
- ❑ Winter Sports
- ❑

Facilities:

- ❑ ADA
- ❑ Gift Shop
- ❑ Museum
- ❑ Visitor Center
- ❑ Restrooms

- ❑ Playground
- ❑ Picnic sites
- ❑
- ❑
- ❑

Memories of the Trip

Get the Facts

- ❑ Phone   (585) 336-6070
- ❑ Park Hours

  _____

- ❑ Reservations? ____Y ____N

  date made_____

- ❑ Open all year? ____Y____N

  dates_____

- ❑ Dog friendly _____Y _____N
- ❑ Distance from home

  miles: _____

  hours: _____

- ❑ Address_____

  _____

  _____

Fees:

- ❑ Day Use $ _____
- ❑ Refund policy

  _____

  _____

  _____

Stamps & Stickers

Oak Orchard State Marine Park
City: Carlton   County: Orleans

Plan your trip: https://parks.ny.gov/parks/oakorchard/details.aspx

Activities: (check all that apply)

- ❑ Beach
- ❑ Biking
- ❑ Boating
- ❑ Canoeing
- ❑ Fishing / Ice
- ❑ Hiking
- ❑ Horseback Riding
- ❑ Hunting
- ❑ Kayaking

- ❑ Marina
- ❑ Nature Center
- ❑ Photography
- ❑ Swimming
- ❑ Waterfalls
- ❑ Watersports
- ❑ Wildlife & Birding
- ❑ Winter Sports
- ❑

Facilities:

- ❑ ADA
- ❑ Gift Shop
- ❑ Museum
- ❑ Visitor Center
- ❑ Restrooms

- ❑ Playground
- ❑ Picnic sites
- ❑
- ❑
- ❑

Memories of the Trip

Get the Facts

- ❑ Phone   (585) 682-4888
- ❑ Park Hours

_____

- ❑ Reservations? ____Y ____N

date made_____

- ❑ Open all year? ____Y____N

dates_____

- ❑ Dog friendly ____Y ____N
- ❑ Distance from home

miles: _____

hours: _____

- ❑ Address_____

_____

_____

Fees:

- ❑ Day Use $ _____
- ❑ Refund policy

_____

_____

_____

Stamps & Stickers

Genesee Valley Greenway State Park
City: Castile   County: Wyoming

Plan your trip: https://parks.ny.gov/parks/geneseevalleygreenway/details.aspx

Activities: (check all that apply)

- ❑ Beach
- ❑ Biking
- ❑ Boating
- ❑ Canoeing
- ❑ Fishing / Ice
- ❑ Hiking
- ❑ Horseback Riding
- ❑ Hunting
- ❑ Kayaking

- ❑ Marina
- ❑ Nature Center
- ❑ Photography
- ❑ Swimming
- ❑ Waterfalls
- ❑ Watersports
- ❑ Wildlife & Birding
- ❑ Winter Sports
- ❑

Facilities:

- ❑ ADA
- ❑ Gift Shop
- ❑ Museum
- ❑ Visitor Center
- ❑ Restrooms

- ❑ Playground
- ❑ Picnic sites
- ❑
- ❑
- ❑

Memories of the Trip

_____
_____
_____
_____
_____
_____
_____
_____
_____
_____
_____
_____
_____
_____
_____
_____
_____

Get the Facts

- ❑ Phone   (585) 493-3614
- ❑ Park Hours

_____

- ❑ Reservations? _____Y _____N

  date made_____

- ❑ Open all year? _____Y_____N

  dates_____

- ❑ Dog friendly _____Y _____N

- ❑ Distance from home

  miles: _____

  hours: _____

- ❑ Address_____

_____

_____

Fees:

- ❑ Day Use $ _____
- ❑ Refund policy

_____

_____

_____

Stamps & Stickers

Silver Lake State Park
City: Castile   County: Wyoming

Plan your trip: https://parks.ny.gov/parks/silverlake/details.aspx

Activities: (check all that apply)

- ❑ Beach
- ❑ Biking
- ❑ Boating
- ❑ Canoeing
- ❑ Fishing / Ice
- ❑ Hiking
- ❑ Horseback Riding
- ❑ Hunting
- ❑ Kayaking

- ❑ Marina
- ❑ Nature Center
- ❑ Photography
- ❑ Swimming
- ❑ Waterfalls
- ❑ Watersports
- ❑ Wildlife & Birding
- ❑ Winter Sports
- ❑

Facilities:

- ❑ ADA
- ❑ Gift Shop
- ❑ Museum
- ❑ Visitor Center
- ❑ Restrooms

- ❑ Playground
- ❑ Picnic sites
- ❑
- ❑
- ❑

Memories of the Trip

Get the Facts

- ❑ Phone   (585) 493-3600
- ❑ Park Hours

  _____

- ❑ Reservations? ____Y ____N

  date made_____

- ❑ Open all year? ____Y____N

  dates_____

- ❑ Dog friendly _____Y _____N
- ❑ Distance from home

  miles: _____

  hours: _____

- ❑ Address_____

  _____

  _____

Fees:

- ❑ Day Use $ _____
- ❑ Refund policy

  _____

  _____

  _____

Stamps & Stickers

Allegany Region

- Cattaraugus County
- Chautauqua County

Allegany State Park - Quaker Area

City: Salamanca   **County: Cattaraugus**

Plan your trip: https://parks.ny.gov/parks/alleganyquaker/details.aspx

Activities:

- ❑ Biking
- ❑ Boating
- ❑ Canoeing
- ❑ Disc Golf
- ❑ Fishing / Ice
- ❑ Hiking
- ❑ Horseback Riding
- ❑ Hunting
- ❑ Kayaking
- ❑ Marina
- ❑ Nature Center / Trails

- ❑ Photography
- ❑ Playing Fields
- ❑ Scenic Views
- ❑ Swimming
- ❑ Waterfalls
- ❑ Wildlife & Birding
- ❑ Winter Sports
- ❑
- ❑
- ❑
- ❑

Facilities:

- ❑ ADA
- ❑ Picnic sites
- ❑ Restrooms
- ❑ Showers
- ❑ Trailer Access
- ❑ Visitor center

- ❑ Group Camping
- ❑ RV Camp
- ❑ Rustic Camping
- ❑ Cabins / Yurts
- ❑ Day Use Area
- ❑

Notes:

Get the Facts

- ❑ Phone   (716) 354-2182
- ❑ Park Hours

  _____

- ❑ Reservations? _____Y _____N

  date made_____

- ❑ Open all year _____Y_____N

  dates_____

- ❑ Check in time _____
- ❑ Check out time _____
- ❑ Pet friendly _____Y _____N
- ❑ Max RV length _____
- ❑ Distance from home

  miles: _____

  hours: _____

- ❑ Address_____

  _____

  _____

Fees:

- ❑ Day Use $ _____
- ❑ Camp Sites $ _____
- ❑ RV Sites $ _____
- ❑ Refund policy

  _____

  _____

  _____

Make It Personal

Trip dates: _____ | The weather was: Sunny Cloudy Rainy Stormy Snowy Foggy Warm Cold

Why I went:
_____
_____

How I got there: (circle all that apply) Plane Train Car Bus Bike Hike RV MC
_____

I went with:
_____

We stayed in (space, cabin # etc):
_____

Most relaxing day:
_____
_____

Something funny:
_____
_____

Someone we met:
_____
_____

Best story told:
_____
_____

The kids liked this:
_____
_____

The best food:
_____
_____

Games played:
_____
_____

Something disappointing:
_____
_____

Next time I'll do this differently:
_____
_____

Allegany State Park - Red House Area
City: Salamanca   County: Cattaraugus

Plan your trip: https://parks.ny.gov/parks/alleganyredhouse/details.aspx

Activities:

- ❑ Biking
- ❑ Boating
- ❑ Canoeing
- ❑ Disc Golf
- ❑ Fishing / Ice
- ❑ Hiking
- ❑ Horseback Riding
- ❑ Hunting
- ❑ Kayaking
- ❑ Marina
- ❑ Nature Center / Trails

- ❑ Photography
- ❑ Playing Fields
- ❑ Scenic Views
- ❑ Swimming
- ❑ Waterfalls
- ❑ Wildlife & Birding
- ❑ Winter Sports
- ❑
- ❑
- ❑
- ❑

Facilities:

- ❑ ADA
- ❑ Picnic sites
- ❑ Restrooms
- ❑ Showers
- ❑ Trailer Access
- ❑ Visitor center

- ❑ Group Camping
- ❑ RV Camp
- ❑ Rustic Camping
- ❑ Cabins / Yurts
- ❑ Day Use Area
- ❑

Notes:

Get the Facts

- ❑ Phone   (716) 354-9121
- ❑ Park Hours

  _____

- ❑ Reservations? ____Y ____N

  date made_____

- ❑ Open all year ____Y ____N

  dates_____

- ❑ Check in time _____
- ❑ Check out time _____
- ❑ Pet friendly _____Y _____N
- ❑ Max RV length _____
- ❑ Distance from home

  miles: _____

  hours: _____

- ❑ Address_____

  _____

  _____

Fees:

- ❑ Day Use $ _____
- ❑ Camp Sites $ _____
- ❑ RV Sites $ _____
- ❑ Refund policy

  _____

  _____

  _____

Make It Personal

Trip dates: _____ | The weather was: Sunny Cloudy Rainy Stormy Snowy Foggy Warm Cold

Why I went:

_____

_____

How I got there: (circle all that apply)   Plane   Train   Car   Bus   Bike   Hike   RV   MC

I went with:

_____

We stayed in (space, cabin # etc):

_____

Most relaxing day:

_____

Something funny:

_____

Someone we met:

_____

Best story told:

_____

The kids liked this:

_____

The best food:

_____

Games played:

_____

Something disappointing:

_____

Next time I'll do this differently:

_____

_____

Lake Erie State Park
City: Brocton   County: Chautauqua

Plan your trip: https://parks.ny.gov/parks/lakeerie/details.aspx

Activities:

- ❑ Biking
- ❑ Boating
- ❑ Canoeing
- ❑ Disc Golf
- ❑ Fishing / Ice
- ❑ Hiking
- ❑ Horseback Riding
- ❑ Hunting
- ❑ Kayaking
- ❑ Marina
- ❑ Nature Center / Trails

- ❑ Photography
- ❑ Playing Fields
- ❑ Scenic Views
- ❑ Swimming
- ❑ Waterfalls
- ❑ Wildlife & Birding
- ❑ Winter Sports
- ❑
- ❑
- ❑
- ❑

Facilities:

- ❑ ADA
- ❑ Picnic sites
- ❑ Restrooms
- ❑ Showers
- ❑ Trailer Access
- ❑ Visitor center

- ❑ Group Camping
- ❑ RV Camp
- ❑ Rustic Camping
- ❑ Cabins / Yurts
- ❑ Day Use Area
- ❑

Notes:

Get the Facts

- ❑ Phone   (716) 792-9214
- ❑ Park Hours

_____

- ❑ Reservations? ____Y ____N

date made_____

- ❑ Open all year ____Y_____N

dates_____

- ❑ Check in time _____
- ❑ Check out time _____
- ❑ Pet friendly _____Y _____N
- ❑ Max RV length _____
- ❑ Distance from home

miles: _____

hours: _____

- ❑ Address_____

_____

_____

Fees:

- ❑ Day Use $ _____
- ❑ Camp Sites $ _____
- ❑ RV Sites $ _____
- ❑ Refund policy

_____

_____

_____

Make It Personal

Trip dates: _____ | The weather was: Sunny Cloudy Rainy Stormy Snowy Foggy Warm Cold

Why I went: _____

_____

How I got there: (circle all that apply) Plane Train Car Bus Bike Hike RV MC

I went with: _____

We stayed in (space, cabin # etc): _____

Most relaxing day: _____

_____

Something funny: _____

_____

Someone we met: _____

_____

Best story told: _____

_____

The kids liked this: _____

_____

The best food: _____

_____

Games played: _____

_____

Something disappointing: _____

_____

Next time I'll do this differently: _____

_____

Evangola State Park
City: Irving   County: Chautauqua

Plan your trip: https://parks.ny.gov/parks/evangola/details.aspx

Activities:

- ❑ Biking
- ❑ Boating
- ❑ Canoeing
- ❑ Disc Golf
- ❑ Fishing / Ice
- ❑ Hiking
- ❑ Horseback Riding
- ❑ Hunting
- ❑ Kayaking
- ❑ Marina
- ❑ Nature Center / Trails

- ❑ Photography
- ❑ Playing Fields
- ❑ Scenic Views
- ❑ Swimming
- ❑ Waterfalls
- ❑ Wildlife & Birding
- ❑ Winter Sports
- ❑
- ❑
- ❑
- ❑

Facilities:

- ❑ ADA
- ❑ Picnic sites
- ❑ Restrooms
- ❑ Showers
- ❑ Trailer Access
- ❑ Visitor center

- ❑ Group Camping
- ❑ RV Camp
- ❑ Rustic Camping
- ❑ Cabins / Yurts
- ❑ Day Use Area
- ❑

Notes:

Get the Facts

- ❑ Phone   (716) 549-1802
- ❑ Park Hours

  _____

- ❑ Reservations? ____Y ____N

  date made_____

- ❑ Open all year ____Y_____N

  dates_____

- ❑ Check in time _____
- ❑ Check out time _____
- ❑ Pet friendly _____Y _____N
- ❑ Max RV length _____
- ❑ Distance from home

  miles: _____

  hours: _____

- ❑ Address_____

  _____

  _____

Fees:

- ❑ Day Use $ _____
- ❑ Camp Sites $ _____
- ❑ RV Sites $ _____
- ❑ Refund policy

  _____

  _____

  _____

Make It Personal

Trip dates: _____ | The weather was: Sunny Cloudy Rainy Stormy Snowy Foggy Warm Cold

Why I went: _____

How I got there: (circle all that apply) Plane Train Car Bus Bike Hike RV MC

I went with: _____

We stayed in (space, cabin # etc): _____

Most relaxing day: _____

Something funny: _____

Someone we met: _____

Best story told: _____

The kids liked this: _____

The best food: _____

Games played: _____

Something disappointing: _____

Next time I'll do this differently: _____

Long Point State Park on Lake Chautauqua
City: Bemus Point   County: Chautauqua

Plan your trip: https://parks.ny.gov/parks/longpointchautauqua/details.aspx

Activities: (check all that apply)

- ❑ Beach
- ❑ Biking
- ❑ Boating
- ❑ Canoeing
- ❑ Fishing / Ice
- ❑ Hiking
- ❑ Horseback Riding
- ❑ Hunting
- ❑ Kayaking

- ❑ Marina
- ❑ Nature Center
- ❑ Photography
- ❑ Swimming
- ❑ Waterfalls
- ❑ Watersports
- ❑ Wildlife & Birding
- ❑ Winter Sports
- ❑

Facilities:

- ❑ ADA
- ❑ Gift Shop
- ❑ Museum
- ❑ Visitor Center
- ❑ Restrooms

- ❑ Playground
- ❑ Picnic sites
- ❑
- ❑
- ❑

Memories of the Trip

Get the Facts

- ❑ Phone   (716) 386-2722
- ❑ Park Hours

  _____

- ❑ Reservations? _____Y _____N

  date made_____

- ❑ Open all year? _____Y_____N

  dates_____

- ❑ Dog friendly _____Y _____N

- ❑ Distance from home

  miles: _____

  hours: _____

- ❑ Address_____

  _____

  _____

Fees:

- ❑ Day Use $ _____
- ❑ Refund policy

  _____

  _____

  _____

Stamps & Stickers

Midway State Park
City: Bemus Point   County: Chautauqua

Plan your trip: https://parks.ny.gov/parks/midway/details.aspx

Activities: (check all that apply)

- ❑ Beach
- ❑ Biking
- ❑ Boating
- ❑ Canoeing
- ❑ Fishing / Ice
- ❑ Hiking
- ❑ Horseback Riding
- ❑ Hunting
- ❑ Kayaking

- ❑ Marina
- ❑ Nature Center
- ❑ Photography
- ❑ Swimming
- ❑ Waterfalls
- ❑ Watersports
- ❑ Wildlife & Birding
- ❑ Winter Sports
- ❑

Facilities:

- ❑ ADA
- ❑ Gift Shop
- ❑ Museum
- ❑ Visitor Center
- ❑ Restrooms

- ❑ Playground
- ❑ Picnic sites
- ❑
- ❑
- ❑

Memories of the Trip

Get the Facts

- ❑ Phone   (716) 386-3165
- ❑ Park Hours

_____

- ❑ Reservations? _____Y _____N

  date made_____

- ❑ Open all year? _____Y_____N

  dates_____

- ❑ Dog friendly _____Y _____N
- ❑ Distance from home

  miles: _____

  hours: _____

- ❑ Address_____

_____

_____

Fees:

- ❑ Day Use $ _____
- ❑ Refund policy

_____

_____

_____

Stamps & Stickers

Sunset Bay State Marine Park

City: Irving   **County: Chautauqua**

Plan your trip: https://parks.ny.gov/parks/sunsetbay/details.aspx

Activities: (check all that apply)

- ❑ Beach
- ❑ Biking
- ❑ Boating
- ❑ Canoeing
- ❑ Fishing / Ice
- ❑ Hiking
- ❑ Horseback Riding
- ❑ Hunting
- ❑ Kayaking

- ❑ Marina
- ❑ Nature Center
- ❑ Photography
- ❑ Swimming
- ❑ Waterfalls
- ❑ Watersports
- ❑ Wildlife & Birding
- ❑ Winter Sports
- ❑

Facilities:

- ❑ ADA
- ❑ Gift Shop
- ❑ Museum
- ❑ Visitor Center
- ❑ Restrooms

- ❑ Playground
- ❑ Picnic sites
- ❑
- ❑
- ❑

Memories of the Trip

Get the Facts

- ❑ Phone   (716) 934-2375
- ❑ Park Hours

  _____

- ❑ Reservations? _____Y _____N

  date made_____

- ❑ Open all year? _____Y____N

  dates_____

- ❑ Dog friendly _____Y _____N

- ❑ Distance from home

  miles: _____

  hours: _____

- ❑ Address_____

  _____

  _____

Fees:

- ❑ Day Use $ _____
- ❑ Refund policy

  _____

  _____

  _____

Stamps & Stickers

Finger Lakes Region

- Cayuga County
- Chemung County
- Ontario County
- Schuyler County
- Seneca County
- Tioga County
- Tompkins County
- Wayne County
- Yates County

Long Point State Park -Finger Lakes

City: Aurora   County: Cayuga

Plan your trip: https://parks.ny.gov/parks/longpointfingerlakes/details.aspx

Activities:

- ☐ Biking
- ☐ Boating
- ☐ Canoeing
- ☐ Disc Golf
- ☐ Fishing / Ice
- ☐ Hiking
- ☐ Horseback Riding
- ☐ Hunting
- ☐ Kayaking
- ☐ Marina
- ☐ Nature Center / Trails

- ☐ Photography
- ☐ Playing Fields
- ☐ Scenic Views
- ☐ Swimming
- ☐ Waterfalls
- ☐ Wildlife & Birding
- ☐ Winter Sports
- ☐
- ☐
- ☐
- ☐

Facilities:

- ☐ ADA
- ☐ Picnic sites
- ☐ Restrooms
- ☐ Showers
- ☐ Trailer Access
- ☐ Visitor center

- ☐ Group Camping
- ☐ RV Camp
- ☐ Rustic Camping
- ☐ Cabins / Yurts
- ☐ Day Use Area
- ☐

Notes:

Get the Facts

- ☐ Phone   (315) 364-5637
- ☐ Park Hours

  _____

- ☐ Reservations? ____Y ____N

  date made_____

- ☐ Open all year ____Y____N

  dates_____

- ☐ Check in time _____
- ☐ Check out time _____
- ☐ Pet friendly _____Y _____N
- ☐ Max RV length _____
- ☐ Distance from home

  miles: _____

  hours: _____

- ☐ Address_____

  _____

  _____

Fees:

- ☐ Day Use $ _____
- ☐ Camp Sites $ _____
- ☐ RV Sites $ _____
- ☐ Refund policy

  _____

  _____

  _____

Make It Personal

Trip dates: _____ | The weather was: Sunny Cloudy Rainy Stormy Snowy Foggy Warm Cold

Why I went:

_____

_____

How I got there: (circle all that apply)   Plane   Train   Car   Bus   Bike   Hike   RV   MC

_____

I went with:

_____

We stayed in (space, cabin # etc):

_____

Most relaxing day:

_____

_____

Something funny:

_____

_____

Someone we met:

_____

_____

Best story told:

_____

_____

The kids liked this:

_____

_____

The best food:

_____

_____

Games played:

_____

_____

Something disappointing:

_____

_____

Next time I'll do this differently:

_____

_____

Fair Haven Beach State Park
City: Fair Haven   County: Cayuga

Plan your trip: https://parks.ny.gov/parks/fairhavenbeach/details.aspx

Activities:

- ❑ Biking
- ❑ Boating
- ❑ Canoeing
- ❑ Disc Golf
- ❑ Fishing / Ice
- ❑ Hiking
- ❑ Horseback Riding
- ❑ Hunting
- ❑ Kayaking
- ❑ Marina
- ❑ Nature Center / Trails
- ❑ Photography
- ❑ Playing Fields
- ❑ Scenic Views
- ❑ Swimming
- ❑ Waterfalls
- ❑ Wildlife & Birding
- ❑ Winter Sports
- ❑
- ❑
- ❑
- ❑

Facilities:

- ❑ ADA
- ❑ Picnic sites
- ❑ Restrooms
- ❑ Showers
- ❑ Trailer Access
- ❑ Visitor center
- ❑ Group Camping
- ❑ RV Camp
- ❑ Rustic Camping
- ❑ Cabins / Yurts
- ❑ Day Use Area
- ❑

Notes:

Get the Facts

- ❑ Phone   (315) 947-5205
- ❑ Park Hours

  _____

- ❑ Reservations? ____Y ____N

  date made_____

- ❑ Open all year ____Y____N

  dates_____

- ❑ Check in time _____
- ❑ Check out time _____
- ❑ Pet friendly _____Y _____N
- ❑ Max RV length _____
- ❑ Distance from home

  miles: _____

  hours: _____

- ❑ Address_____

  _____

  _____

Fees:

- ❑ Day Use $ _____
- ❑ Camp Sites $ _____
- ❑ RV Sites $ _____
- ❑ Refund policy

  _____

  _____

  _____

Make It Personal

Trip dates: _____ | The weather was: Sunny   Cloudy   Rainy   Stormy   Snowy   Foggy   Warm   Cold

Why I went:

_____

_____

How I got there: (circle all that apply)   Plane   Train   Car   Bus   Bike   Hike   RV   MC

_____

I went with:

_____

We stayed in (space, cabin # etc):

_____

Most relaxing day:

_____

_____

Something funny:

_____

_____

Someone we met:

_____

_____

Best story told:

_____

_____

The kids liked this:

_____

_____

The best food:

_____

_____

Games played:

_____

_____

Something disappointing:

_____

_____

Next time I'll do this differently:

_____

_____

Fillmore Glen State Park
City: Moravia   County: Cayuga

Plan your trip: https://parks.ny.gov/parks/fillmoreglen/details.aspx

Activities:

- ❑ Biking
- ❑ Boating
- ❑ Canoeing
- ❑ Disc Golf
- ❑ Fishing / Ice
- ❑ Hiking
- ❑ Horseback Riding
- ❑ Hunting
- ❑ Kayaking
- ❑ Marina
- ❑ Nature Center / Trails

- ❑ Photography
- ❑ Playing Fields
- ❑ Scenic Views
- ❑ Swimming
- ❑ Waterfalls
- ❑ Wildlife & Birding
- ❑ Winter Sports
- ❑
- ❑
- ❑
- ❑

Facilities:

- ❑ ADA
- ❑ Picnic sites
- ❑ Restrooms
- ❑ Showers
- ❑ Trailer Access
- ❑ Visitor center

- ❑ Group Camping
- ❑ RV Camp
- ❑ Rustic Camping
- ❑ Cabins / Yurts
- ❑ Day Use Area
- ❑

Notes:

Get the Facts

- ❑ Phone   (315) 497-0130
- ❑ Park Hours

  _____

- ❑ Reservations? ____Y ____N

  date made_____

- ❑ Open all year ____Y ____N

  dates_____

- ❑ Check in time _____
- ❑ Check out time _____
- ❑ Pet friendly _____Y ____N
- ❑ Max RV length _____
- ❑ Distance from home

  miles: _____

  hours: _____

- ❑ Address_____

  _____

  _____

Fees:

- ❑ Day Use $ _____
- ❑ Camp Sites $ _____
- ❑ RV Sites $ _____
- ❑ Refund policy

  _____

  _____

  _____

Make It Personal

Trip dates: _____ | The weather was: Sunny Cloudy Rainy Stormy Snowy Foggy Warm Cold

Why I went:
_____

How I got there: (circle all that apply) Plane Train Car Bus Bike Hike RV MC

I went with:
_____

We stayed in (space, cabin # etc):
_____

Most relaxing day:
_____

Something funny:
_____

Someone we met:
_____

Best story told:
_____

The kids liked this:
_____

The best food:
_____

Games played:
_____

Something disappointing:
_____

Next time I'll do this differently:
_____

Newtown Battlefield State Park
City: Elmira   County: Chemung

Plan your trip: https://parks.ny.gov/parks/newtownbattlefield/details.aspx

Activities:

- ❏ Biking
- ❏ Boating
- ❏ Canoeing
- ❏ Disc Golf
- ❏ Fishing / Ice
- ❏ Hiking
- ❏ Horseback Riding
- ❏ Hunting
- ❏ Kayaking
- ❏ Marina
- ❏ Nature Center / Trails
- ❏ Photography
- ❏ Playing Fields
- ❏ Scenic Views
- ❏ Swimming
- ❏ Waterfalls
- ❏ Wildlife & Birding
- ❏ Winter Sports
- ❏
- ❏
- ❏
- ❏

Facilities:

- ❏ ADA
- ❏ Picnic sites
- ❏ Restrooms
- ❏ Showers
- ❏ Trailer Access
- ❏ Visitor center
- ❏ Group Camping
- ❏ RV Camp
- ❏ Rustic Camping
- ❏ Cabins / Yurts
- ❏ Day Use Area
- ❏

Notes:

Get the Facts

- ❏ Phone   (607) 732-6067
- ❏ Park Hours

  _____

- ❏ Reservations? ____Y ____N

  date made_____

- ❏ Open all year ____Y____N

  dates_____

- ❏ Check in time _____
- ❏ Check out time _____
- ❏ Pet friendly _____Y ____N
- ❏ Max RV length _____
- ❏ Distance from home

  miles: _____

  hours: _____

- ❏ Address_____

  _____

  _____

Fees:

- ❏ Day Use $ _____
- ❏ Camp Sites $ _____
- ❏ RV Sites $ _____
- ❏ Refund policy

  _____

  _____

  _____

Make It Personal

Trip dates: _____ | The weather was: Sunny Cloudy Rainy Stormy Snowy Foggy Warm Cold

Why I went:
_____

How I got there: (circle all that apply) Plane Train Car Bus Bike Hike RV MC

I went with:
_____

We stayed in (space, cabin # etc):
_____

Most relaxing day:
_____

Something funny:
_____

Someone we met:
_____

Best story told:
_____

The kids liked this:
_____

The best food:
_____

Games played:
_____

Something disappointing:
_____

Next time I'll do this differently:
_____
_____

Watkins Glen State Park
City: Watkins Glen   County: Schuyler

Plan your trip: https://parks.ny.gov/parks/watkinsglen/details.aspx

Activities:

- ❑ Biking
- ❑ Boating
- ❑ Canoeing
- ❑ Disc Golf
- ❑ Fishing / Ice
- ❑ Hiking
- ❑ Horseback Riding
- ❑ Hunting
- ❑ Kayaking
- ❑ Marina
- ❑ Nature Center / Trails
- ❑ Photography
- ❑ Playing Fields
- ❑ Scenic Views
- ❑ Swimming
- ❑ Waterfalls
- ❑ Wildlife & Birding
- ❑ Winter Sports
- ❑
- ❑
- ❑
- ❑

Facilities:

- ❑ ADA
- ❑ Picnic sites
- ❑ Restrooms
- ❑ Showers
- ❑ Trailer Access
- ❑ Visitor center
- ❑ Group Camping
- ❑ RV Camp
- ❑ Rustic Camping
- ❑ Cabins / Yurts
- ❑ Day Use Area
- ❑

Notes:

Get the Facts

- ❑ Phone   (607) 535-4511
- ❑ Park Hours

_____

- ❑ Reservations? _____Y _____N

date made_____

- ❑ Open all year _____Y_____N

dates_____

- ❑ Check in time _____
- ❑ Check out time _____
- ❑ Pet friendly _____Y _____N
- ❑ Max RV length _____
- ❑ Distance from home

miles: _____

hours: _____

- ❑ Address_____

_____

_____

Fees:

- ❑ Day Use $ _____
- ❑ Camp Sites $ _____
- ❑ RV Sites $ _____
- ❑ Refund policy

_____

_____

_____

Make It Personal

Trip dates: _____ | The weather was: Sunny Cloudy Rainy Stormy Snowy Foggy Warm Cold

Why I went:
_____

_____

How I got there: (circle all that apply)   Plane   Train   Car   Bus   Bike   Hike   RV   MC
_____

I went with:
_____

We stayed in (space, cabin # etc):
_____

Most relaxing day:
_____

_____

Something funny:
_____

_____

Someone we met:
_____

_____

Best story told:
_____

_____

The kids liked this:
_____

_____

The best food:
_____

_____

Games played:
_____

_____

Something disappointing:
_____

_____

Next time I'll do this differently:
_____

_____

Sampson State Park
City: Romulus   County: Seneca

Plan your trip: https://parks.ny.gov/parks/sampson/details.aspx

Activities:

- ☐ Biking
- ☐ Boating
- ☐ Canoeing
- ☐ Disc Golf
- ☐ Fishing / Ice
- ☐ Hiking
- ☐ Horseback Riding
- ☐ Hunting
- ☐ Kayaking
- ☐ Marina
- ☐ Nature Center / Trails

- ☐ Photography
- ☐ Playing Fields
- ☐ Scenic Views
- ☐ Swimming
- ☐ Waterfalls
- ☐ Wildlife & Birding
- ☐ Winter Sports
- ☐
- ☐
- ☐
- ☐

Facilities:

- ☐ ADA
- ☐ Picnic sites
- ☐ Restrooms
- ☐ Showers
- ☐ Trailer Access
- ☐ Visitor center

- ☐ Group Camping
- ☐ RV Camp
- ☐ Rustic Camping
- ☐ Cabins / Yurts
- ☐ Day Use Area
- ☐

Notes:

Get the Facts

- ☐ Phone   (315) 585-6392
- ☐ Park Hours

  _____

- ☐ Reservations? ____Y ____N

  date made_____

- ☐ Open all year ____Y____N

  dates_____

- ☐ Check in time _____
- ☐ Check out time _____
- ☐ Pet friendly _____Y _____N
- ☐ Max RV length _____
- ☐ Distance from home

  miles: _____

  hours: _____

- ☐ Address_____

  _____

  _____

Fees:

- ☐ Day Use $ _____
- ☐ Camp Sites $ _____
- ☐ RV Sites $ _____
- ☐ Refund policy

  _____

  _____

  _____

Make It Personal

Trip dates: _____ | The weather was: Sunny Cloudy Rainy Stormy Snowy Foggy Warm Cold

Why I went:
_____
_____

How I got there: (circle all that apply)   Plane   Train   Car   Bus   Bike   Hike   RV   MC
_____

I went with:
_____

We stayed in (space, cabin # etc):
_____

Most relaxing day:
_____
_____

Something funny:
_____
_____

Someone we met:
_____
_____

Best story told:
_____
_____

The kids liked this:
_____
_____

The best food:
_____
_____

Games played:
_____
_____

Something disappointing:
_____
_____

Next time I'll do this differently:
_____
_____

Cayuga Lake State Park
City: Seneca Falls   County: Seneca

Plan your trip: https://parks.ny.gov/parks/cayugalake/details.aspx

Activities:

- ❑ Biking
- ❑ Boating
- ❑ Canoeing
- ❑ Disc Golf
- ❑ Fishing / Ice
- ❑ Hiking
- ❑ Horseback Riding
- ❑ Hunting
- ❑ Kayaking
- ❑ Marina
- ❑ Nature Center / Trails

- ❑ Photography
- ❑ Playing Fields
- ❑ Scenic Views
- ❑ Swimming
- ❑ Waterfalls
- ❑ Wildlife & Birding
- ❑ Winter Sports
- ❑
- ❑
- ❑
- ❑

Facilities:

- ❑ ADA
- ❑ Picnic sites
- ❑ Restrooms
- ❑ Showers
- ❑ Trailer Access
- ❑ Visitor center

- ❑ Group Camping
- ❑ RV Camp
- ❑ Rustic Camping
- ❑ Cabins / Yurts
- ❑ Day Use Area
- ❑

Notes:

Get the Facts

- ❑ Phone   (315) 568-5163
- ❑ Park Hours

  _____

- ❑ Reservations? _____Y _____N

  date made_____

- ❑ Open all year _____Y_____N

  dates_____

- ❑ Check in time _____
- ❑ Check out time _____
- ❑ Pet friendly _____Y _____N
- ❑ Max RV length _____
- ❑ Distance from home

  miles: _____

  hours: _____

- ❑ Address_____

  _____

  _____

Fees:

- ❑ Day Use $ _____
- ❑ Camp Sites $ _____
- ❑ RV Sites $ _____
- ❑ Refund policy

  _____

  _____

  _____

Make It Personal

Trip dates: _____ | The weather was: Sunny Cloudy Rainy Stormy Snowy Foggy Warm Cold

Why I went: _____

_____

How I got there: (circle all that apply) Plane   Train   Car   Bus   Bike   Hike   RV   MC

I went with: _____

We stayed in (space, cabin # etc): _____

Most relaxing day: _____

_____

Something funny: _____

_____

Someone we met: _____

_____

Best story told: _____

_____

The kids liked this: _____

_____

The best food: _____

_____

Games played: _____

_____

Something disappointing: _____

_____

Next time I'll do this differently: _____

_____

Robert H. Treman State Park
City: Ithaca   County: Tompkins

Plan your trip: https://parks.ny.gov/parks/roberttreman/details.aspx

Activities:

- ☐ Biking
- ☐ Boating
- ☐ Canoeing
- ☐ Disc Golf
- ☐ Fishing / Ice
- ☐ Hiking
- ☐ Horseback Riding
- ☐ Hunting
- ☐ Kayaking
- ☐ Marina
- ☐ Nature Center / Trails

- ☐ Photography
- ☐ Playing Fields
- ☐ Scenic Views
- ☐ Swimming
- ☐ Waterfalls
- ☐ Wildlife & Birding
- ☐ Winter Sports
- ☐
- ☐
- ☐
- ☐

Facilities:

- ☐ ADA
- ☐ Picnic sites
- ☐ Restrooms
- ☐ Showers
- ☐ Trailer Access
- ☐ Visitor center

- ☐ Group Camping
- ☐ RV Camp
- ☐ Rustic Camping
- ☐ Cabins / Yurts
- ☐ Day Use Area
- ☐

Notes:

Get the Facts

- ☐ Phone   (607) 273-3440
- ☐ Park Hours

  _____

- ☐ Reservations? ____Y ____N

  date made_____

- ☐ Open all year ____Y____N

  dates_____

- ☐ Check in time _____
- ☐ Check out time _____
- ☐ Pet friendly _____Y _____N
- ☐ Max RV length _____
- ☐ Distance from home

  miles: _____

  hours: _____

- ☐ Address_____

  _____

  _____

Fees:

- ☐ Day Use $ _____
- ☐ Camp Sites $ _____
- ☐ RV Sites $ _____
- ☐ Refund policy

  _____

  _____

  _____

Make It Personal

Trip dates: _____ | The weather was: Sunny Cloudy Rainy Stormy Snowy Foggy Warm Cold

Why I went:
_____

How I got there: (circle all that apply)   Plane   Train   Car   Bus   Bike   Hike   RV   MC
_____

I went with:
_____

We stayed in (space, cabin # etc):
_____

Most relaxing day:
_____

Something funny:
_____

Someone we met:
_____

Best story told:
_____

The kids liked this:
_____

The best food:
_____

Games played:
_____

Something disappointing:
_____

Next time I'll do this differently:
_____
_____

Buttermilk Falls State Park

City: Ithaca   **County: Tompkins**

Plan your trip: https://parks.ny.gov/parks/buttermilkfalls/details.aspx

Activities:

- ❑ Biking
- ❑ Boating
- ❑ Canoeing
- ❑ Disc Golf
- ❑ Fishing / Ice
- ❑ Hiking
- ❑ Horseback Riding
- ❑ Hunting
- ❑ Kayaking
- ❑ Marina
- ❑ Nature Center / Trails

- ❑ Photography
- ❑ Playing Fields
- ❑ Scenic Views
- ❑ Swimming
- ❑ Waterfalls
- ❑ Wildlife & Birding
- ❑ Winter Sports
- ❑
- ❑
- ❑
- ❑

Facilities:

- ❑ ADA
- ❑ Picnic sites
- ❑ Restrooms
- ❑ Showers
- ❑ Trailer Access
- ❑ Visitor center

- ❑ Group Camping
- ❑ RV Camp
- ❑ Rustic Camping
- ❑ Cabins / Yurts
- ❑ Day Use Area
- ❑

Notes:

Get the Facts

- ❑ Phone   (607) 273-5761
- ❑ Park Hours

  _____
- ❑ Reservations? _____Y _____N

  date made_____
- ❑ Open all year _____Y _____N

  dates_____
- ❑ Check in time _____
- ❑ Check out time _____
- ❑ Pet friendly _____Y _____N
- ❑ Max RV length _____
- ❑ Distance from home

  miles: _____

  hours: _____
- ❑ Address_____

  _____

  _____

Fees:

- ❑ Day Use $ _____
- ❑ Camp Sites $ _____
- ❑ RV Sites $ _____
- ❑ Refund policy

  _____

  _____

  _____

Make It Personal

Trip dates: _____ | The weather was: Sunny Cloudy Rainy Stormy Snowy Foggy Warm Cold

_____

Why I went:

_____

_____

How I got there: (circle all that apply)   Plane   Train   Car   Bus   Bike   Hike   RV   MC

_____

I went with:

_____

We stayed in (space, cabin # etc):

_____

Most relaxing day:

_____

_____

Something funny:

_____

_____

Someone we met:

_____

_____

Best story told:

_____

_____

The kids liked this:

_____

_____

The best food:

_____

_____

Games played:

_____

_____

Something disappointing:

_____

_____

Next time I'll do this differently:

_____

_____

Taughannock Falls State Park
City: Trumansburg   County: Tompkins

Plan your trip: https://parks.ny.gov/parks/taughannockfalls/details.aspx

Activities:

- ❑ Biking
- ❑ Boating
- ❑ Canoeing
- ❑ Disc Golf
- ❑ Fishing / Ice
- ❑ Hiking
- ❑ Horseback Riding
- ❑ Hunting
- ❑ Kayaking
- ❑ Marina
- ❑ Nature Center / Trails
- ❑ Photography
- ❑ Playing Fields
- ❑ Scenic Views
- ❑ Swimming
- ❑ Waterfalls
- ❑ Wildlife & Birding
- ❑ Winter Sports
- ❑
- ❑
- ❑
- ❑

Facilities:

- ❑ ADA
- ❑ Picnic sites
- ❑ Restrooms
- ❑ Showers
- ❑ Trailer Access
- ❑ Visitor center
- ❑ Group Camping
- ❑ RV Camp
- ❑ Rustic Camping
- ❑ Cabins / Yurts
- ❑ Day Use Area
- ❑

Notes:

Get the Facts

- ❑ Phone   (607) 387-6739
- ❑ Park Hours

  _____

- ❑ Reservations? _____Y _____N

  date made_____

- ❑ Open all year _____Y_____N

  dates_____

- ❑ Check in time _____
- ❑ Check out time _____
- ❑ Pet friendly _____Y _____N
- ❑ Max RV length _____
- ❑ Distance from home

  miles: _____

  hours: _____

- ❑ Address_____

  _____

  _____

Fees:

- ❑ Day Use $ _____
- ❑ Camp Sites $ _____
- ❑ RV Sites $ _____
- ❑ Refund policy

  _____

  _____

  _____

Make It Personal

Trip dates: _____ | The weather was: Sunny Cloudy Rainy Stormy Snowy Foggy Warm Cold

Why I went:

_____

How I got there: (circle all that apply)   Plane   Train   Car   Bus   Bike   Hike   RV   MC

I went with:
_____

We stayed in (space, cabin # etc):
_____

Most relaxing day:

_____

Something funny:

_____

Someone we met:

_____

Best story told:

_____

The kids liked this:

_____

The best food:

_____

Games played:

_____

Something disappointing:

_____

Next time I'll do this differently:

_____

Keuka Lake State Park
City: Bluff Point   County: Yates

Plan your trip: https://parks.ny.gov/parks/keukalake/details.aspx

Activities:

- ❑ Biking
- ❑ Boating
- ❑ Canoeing
- ❑ Disc Golf
- ❑ Fishing / Ice
- ❑ Hiking
- ❑ Horseback Riding
- ❑ Hunting
- ❑ Kayaking
- ❑ Marina
- ❑ Nature Center / Trails

- ❑ Photography
- ❑ Playing Fields
- ❑ Scenic Views
- ❑ Swimming
- ❑ Waterfalls
- ❑ Wildlife & Birding
- ❑ Winter Sports
- ❑
- ❑
- ❑
- ❑

Facilities:

- ❑ ADA
- ❑ Picnic sites
- ❑ Restrooms
- ❑ Showers
- ❑ Trailer Access
- ❑ Visitor center

- ❑ Group Camping
- ❑ RV Camp
- ❑ Rustic Camping
- ❑ Cabins / Yurts
- ❑ Day Use Area
- ❑

Notes:

Get the Facts

- ❑ Phone   (315) 536-3666
- ❑ Park Hours

  _____

- ❑ Reservations? ____Y ____N

  date made_____

- ❑ Open all year ____Y____N

  dates_____

- ❑ Check in time _____
- ❑ Check out time _____
- ❑ Pet friendly _____Y ____N
- ❑ Max RV length _____
- ❑ Distance from home

  miles: _____

  hours: _____

- ❑ Address_____

  _____

  _____

Fees:

- ❑ Day Use $ _____
- ❑ Camp Sites $ _____
- ❑ RV Sites $ _____
- ❑ Refund policy

  _____

  _____

  _____

Make It Personal

Trip dates: _____ | The weather was: Sunny Cloudy Rainy Stormy Snowy Foggy Warm Cold

Why I went:
_____

_____

How I got there: (circle all that apply)   Plane   Train   Car   Bus   Bike   Hike   RV   MC
_____

I went with:
_____

We stayed in (space, cabin # etc):
_____

Most relaxing day:
_____

_____

Something funny:
_____

_____

Someone we met:
_____

_____

Best story told:
_____

_____

The kids liked this:
_____

_____

The best food:
_____

_____

Games played:
_____

_____

Something disappointing:
_____

_____

Next time I'll do this differently:
_____

_____

Mark Twain State Park
City: Horseheads   County: Chemung

Plan your trip: https://parks.ny.gov/parks/138/details.aspx

Activities: (check all that apply)

- ❑ Beach
- ❑ Biking
- ❑ Boating
- ❑ Canoeing
- ❑ Fishing / Ice
- ❑ Hiking
- ❑ Horseback Riding
- ❑ Hunting
- ❑ Kayaking

- ❑ Marina
- ❑ Nature Center
- ❑ Photography
- ❑ Swimming
- ❑ Waterfalls
- ❑ Watersports
- ❑ Wildlife & Birding
- ❑ Winter Sports
- ❑

Facilities:

- ❑ ADA
- ❑ Gift Shop
- ❑ Museum
- ❑ Visitor Center
- ❑ Restrooms

- ❑ Playground
- ❑ Picnic sites
- ❑
- ❑
- ❑

Memories of the Trip

Get the Facts

- ❑ Phone   (607) 739-0034
- ❑ Park Hours

  _____

- ❑ Reservations? ____Y ____N

  date made_____

- ❑ Open all year? ____Y____N

  dates_____

- ❑ Dog friendly _____Y _____N

- ❑ Distance from home

  miles: _____

  hours: _____

- ❑ Address_____

  _____

  _____

Fees:

- ❑ Day Use $ _____
- ❑ Refund policy

  _____

  _____

  _____

Stamps & Stickers

Canandaigua Lake State Marine Park
City: Canadaigua   County: Ontario

Plan your trip: https://parks.ny.gov/parks/canandaigualake/details.aspx

Activities: (check all that apply)

- ❑ Beach
- ❑ Biking
- ❑ Boating
- ❑ Canoeing
- ❑ Fishing / Ice
- ❑ Hiking
- ❑ Horseback Riding
- ❑ Hunting
- ❑ Kayaking

- ❑ Marina
- ❑ Nature Center
- ❑ Photography
- ❑ Swimming
- ❑ Waterfalls
- ❑ Watersports
- ❑ Wildlife & Birding
- ❑ Winter Sports
- ❑

Facilities:

- ❑ ADA
- ❑ Gift Shop
- ❑ Museum
- ❑ Visitor Center
- ❑ Restrooms

- ❑ Playground
- ❑ Picnic sites
- ❑
- ❑
- ❑

Memories of the Trip

Get the Facts

- ❑ Phone   (585) 394-9420
- ❑ Park Hours

  _____

- ❑ Reservations? _____Y _____N

  date made_____

- ❑ Open all year? _____Y_____N

  dates_____

- ❑ Dog friendly _____Y _____N
- ❑ Distance from home

  miles: _____

  hours: _____

- ❑ Address_____

  _____

  _____

Fees:

- ❑ Day Use $ _____
- ❑ Refund policy

  _____

  _____

  _____

Stamps & Stickers

Seneca Lake State Park
City: Geneva   County: Ontario

Plan your trip: https://parks.ny.gov/parks/senecalake/details.aspx

Activities: (check all that apply)

- ❑ Beach
- ❑ Biking
- ❑ Boating
- ❑ Canoeing
- ❑ Fishing / Ice
- ❑ Hiking
- ❑ Horseback Riding
- ❑ Hunting
- ❑ Kayaking

- ❑ Marina
- ❑ Nature Center
- ❑ Photography
- ❑ Swimming
- ❑ Waterfalls
- ❑ Watersports
- ❑ Wildlife & Birding
- ❑ Winter Sports
- ❑

Facilities:

- ❑ ADA
- ❑ Gift Shop
- ❑ Museum
- ❑ Visitor Center
- ❑ Restrooms

- ❑ Playground
- ❑ Picnic sites
- ❑
- ❑
- ❑

Memories of the Trip

Get the Facts

- ❑ Phone   (315) 789-2331
- ❑ Park Hours

  _____

- ❑ Reservations? _____Y _____N

  date made_____

- ❑ Open all year? _____Y_____N

  dates_____

- ❑ Dog friendly _____Y _____N

- ❑ Distance from home

  miles: _____

  hours: _____

- ❑ Address_____

  _____

  _____

Fees:

- ❑ Day Use $ _____
- ❑ Refund policy

  _____

  _____

  _____

Stamps & Stickers

Lodi Point State Park
City: Lodi   County: Seneca

Plan your trip: https://parks.ny.gov/parks/lodipoint/details.aspx

Activities: (check all that apply)

- ❑ Beach
- ❑ Biking
- ❑ Boating
- ❑ Canoeing
- ❑ Fishing / Ice
- ❑ Hiking
- ❑ Horseback Riding
- ❑ Hunting
- ❑ Kayaking

- ❑ Marina
- ❑ Nature Center
- ❑ Photography
- ❑ Swimming
- ❑ Waterfalls
- ❑ Watersports
- ❑ Wildlife & Birding
- ❑ Winter Sports
- ❑

Facilities:

- ❑ ADA
- ❑ Gift Shop
- ❑ Museum
- ❑ Visitor Center
- ❑ Restrooms

- ❑ Playground
- ❑ Picnic sites
- ❑
- ❑
- ❑

Memories of the Trip

Get the Facts

- ❑ Phone   (315) 585-6392
- ❑ Park Hours

  _____

- ❑ Reservations? ____Y ____N

  date made_____

- ❑ Open all year? ____Y____N

  dates_____

- ❑ Dog friendly _____Y _____N
- ❑ Distance from home

  miles: _____

  hours: _____

- ❑ Address_____

  _____

  _____

Fees:

- ❑ Day Use $ _____
- ❑ Refund policy

  _____

  _____

  _____

Stamps & Stickers

Bonavista State Park
City: Ovid   County: Seneca

Plan your trip: https://parks.ny.gov/parks/Bonavista/details.aspx

Activities: (check all that apply)

- ❑ Beach
- ❑ Biking
- ❑ Boating
- ❑ Canoeing
- ❑ Fishing / Ice
- ❑ Hiking
- ❑ Horseback Riding
- ❑ Hunting
- ❑ Kayaking

- ❑ Marina
- ❑ Nature Center
- ❑ Photography
- ❑ Swimming
- ❑ Waterfalls
- ❑ Watersports
- ❑ Wildlife & Birding
- ❑ Winter Sports
- ❑

Facilities:

- ❑ ADA
- ❑ Gift Shop
- ❑ Museum
- ❑ Visitor Center
- ❑ Restrooms

- ❑ Playground
- ❑ Picnic sites
- ❑
- ❑
- ❑

Memories of the Trip

Get the Facts

- ❑ Phone   (607) 869-5482
- ❑ Park Hours

  _____

- ❑ Reservations? _____Y _____N

  date made_____

- ❑ Open all year? _____Y_____N

  dates_____

- ❑ Dog friendly _____Y _____N

- ❑ Distance from home

  miles: _____

  hours: _____

- ❑ Address_____

  _____

  _____

Fees:

- ❑ Day Use $ _____
- ❑ Refund policy

  _____

  _____

  _____

Stamps & Stickers

Two Rivers State Park Recreation Area
City: Waverly   County: Tioga

Plan your trip: https://parks.ny.gov/parks/tworivers/details.aspx

Activities: (check all that apply)

- ❑ Beach
- ❑ Biking
- ❑ Boating
- ❑ Canoeing
- ❑ Fishing / Ice
- ❑ Hiking
- ❑ Horseback Riding
- ❑ Hunting
- ❑ Kayaking

- ❑ Marina
- ❑ Nature Center
- ❑ Photography
- ❑ Swimming
- ❑ Waterfalls
- ❑ Watersports
- ❑ Wildlife & Birding
- ❑ Winter Sports
- ❑

Facilities:

- ❑ ADA
- ❑ Gift Shop
- ❑ Museum
- ❑ Visitor Center
- ❑ Restrooms

- ❑ Playground
- ❑ Picnic sites
- ❑
- ❑
- ❑

Memories of the Trip

Get the Facts

- ❑ Phone   (607) 732-6287
- ❑ Park Hours

  _____

- ❑ Reservations? _____Y _____N

  date made_____

- ❑ Open all year? _____Y_____N

  dates_____

- ❑ Dog friendly _____Y _____N

- ❑ Distance from home

  miles: _____

  hours: _____

- ❑ Address_____

  _____

  _____

Fees:

- ❑ Day Use $ _____
- ❑ Refund policy

  _____

  _____

  _____

Stamps & Stickers

Allan H. Treman State Marine Park

City: Ithaca   County: Tompkins

Plan your trip: https://parks.ny.gov/parks/AllanTreman/details.aspx

Activities: (check all that apply)

- ❑ Beach
- ❑ Biking
- ❑ Boating
- ❑ Canoeing
- ❑ Fishing / Ice
- ❑ Hiking
- ❑ Horseback Riding
- ❑ Hunting
- ❑ Kayaking
- ❑ Marina
- ❑ Nature Center
- ❑ Photography
- ❑ Swimming
- ❑ Waterfalls
- ❑ Watersports
- ❑ Wildlife & Birding
- ❑ Winter Sports
- ❑

Facilities:

- ❑ ADA
- ❑ Gift Shop
- ❑ Museum
- ❑ Visitor Center
- ❑ Restrooms
- ❑ Playground
- ❑ Picnic sites
- ❑
- ❑
- ❑

Memories of the Trip

Get the Facts

- ❑ Phone   (607) 272-1460
- ❑ Park Hours

_____

- ❑ Reservations? ____Y ____N

date made_____

- ❑ Open all year? ____Y____N

dates_____

- ❑ Dog friendly _____Y _____N
- ❑ Distance from home

miles: _____

hours: _____

- ❑ Address_____

_____

_____

Fees:

- ❑ Day Use $ _____
- ❑ Refund policy

_____

_____

_____

Stamps & Stickers

Chimney Bluffs State Park
City: Wolcott　　　　　　County: Wayne

Plan your trip: https://parks.ny.gov/parks/chimneybluffs/details.aspx

Activities: (check all that apply)

- ❑ Beach
- ❑ Biking
- ❑ Boating
- ❑ Canoeing
- ❑ Fishing / Ice
- ❑ Hiking
- ❑ Horseback Riding
- ❑ Hunting
- ❑ Kayaking

- ❑ Marina
- ❑ Nature Center
- ❑ Photography
- ❑ Swimming
- ❑ Waterfalls
- ❑ Watersports
- ❑ Wildlife & Birding
- ❑ Winter Sports
- ❑

Facilities:

- ❑ ADA
- ❑ Gift Shop
- ❑ Museum
- ❑ Visitor Center
- ❑ Restrooms

- ❑ Playground
- ❑ Picnic sites
- ❑
- ❑
- ❑

Memories of the Trip

Get the Facts

- ❑ Phone　(315) 947-5205
- ❑ Park Hours

  _____

- ❑ Reservations? ____Y ____N

  date made_____

- ❑ Open all year? ____Y____N

  dates_____

- ❑ Dog friendly _____Y _____N
- ❑ Distance from home

  miles: _____

  hours: _____

- ❑ Address_____

  _____

  _____

Fees:

- ❑ Day Use $ _____
- ❑ Refund policy

  _____

  _____

  _____

Stamps & Stickers

Notes:

Central Region

- Broome County
- Chenango County
- Delaware County
- Madison County
- Onondaga County
- Oswego County
- Otsego County

Chenango Valley State Park
City: Chenango Forks   County: Broome

Plan your trip: https://parks.ny.gov/parks/chenangovalley/details.aspx

Activities:

- ❑ Biking
- ❑ Boating
- ❑ Canoeing
- ❑ Disc Golf
- ❑ Fishing / Ice
- ❑ Hiking
- ❑ Horseback Riding
- ❑ Hunting
- ❑ Kayaking
- ❑ Marina
- ❑ Nature Center / Trails

- ❑ Photography
- ❑ Playing Fields
- ❑ Scenic Views
- ❑ Swimming
- ❑ Waterfalls
- ❑ Wildlife & Birding
- ❑ Winter Sports
- ❑
- ❑
- ❑
- ❑

Facilities:

- ❑ ADA
- ❑ Picnic sites
- ❑ Restrooms
- ❑ Showers
- ❑ Trailer Access
- ❑ Visitor center

- ❑ Group Camping
- ❑ RV Camp
- ❑ Rustic Camping
- ❑ Cabins / Yurts
- ❑ Day Use Area
- ❑

Notes:

Get the Facts

- ❑ Phone   (607) 648-5251
- ❑ Park Hours

  _____

- ❑ Reservations? ____Y ____N

  date made_____

- ❑ Open all year ____Y_____N

  dates_____

- ❑ Check in time _____
- ❑ Check out time _____
- ❑ Pet friendly _____Y _____N
- ❑ Max RV length _____
- ❑ Distance from home

  miles: _____

  hours: _____

- ❑ Address_____

  _____

  _____

Fees:

- ❑ Day Use $ _____
- ❑ Camp Sites $ _____
- ❑ RV Sites $ _____
- ❑ Refund policy

  _____

  _____

  _____

Make It Personal

Trip dates: _____ | The weather was: Sunny Cloudy Rainy Stormy Snowy Foggy Warm Cold

Why I went: _____

_____

How I got there: (circle all that apply)   Plane   Train   Car   Bus   Bike   Hike   RV   MC

I went with: _____

We stayed in (space, cabin # etc): _____

Most relaxing day: _____

_____

Something funny: _____

_____

Someone we met: _____

_____

Best story told: _____

_____

The kids liked this: _____

_____

The best food: _____

_____

Games played: _____

_____

Something disappointing: _____

_____

Next time I'll do this differently: _____

_____

Oquaga Creek State Park
City: Bainbridge   County: Chenango

Plan your trip: https://parks.ny.gov/parks/oquagacreek/details.aspx

Activities:

- ❏ Biking
- ❏ Boating
- ❏ Canoeing
- ❏ Disc Golf
- ❏ Fishing / Ice
- ❏ Hiking
- ❏ Horseback Riding
- ❏ Hunting
- ❏ Kayaking
- ❏ Marina
- ❏ Nature Center / Trails

- ❏ Photography
- ❏ Playing Fields
- ❏ Scenic Views
- ❏ Swimming
- ❏ Waterfalls
- ❏ Wildlife & Birding
- ❏ Winter Sports
- ❏
- ❏
- ❏
- ❏

Facilities:

- ❏ ADA
- ❏ Picnic sites
- ❏ Restrooms
- ❏ Showers
- ❏ Trailer Access
- ❏ Visitor center

- ❏ Group Camping
- ❏ RV Camp
- ❏ Rustic Camping
- ❏ Cabins / Yurts
- ❏ Day Use Area
- ❏

Notes:

Get the Facts

- ❏ Phone   (607) 467-4160
- ❏ Park Hours

  _____

- ❏ Reservations? _____Y _____N

  date made_____

- ❏ Open all year _____Y _____N

  dates_____

- ❏ Check in time _____
- ❏ Check out time _____
- ❏ Pet friendly _____Y _____N
- ❏ Max RV length _____
- ❏ Distance from home

  miles: _____

  hours: _____

- ❏ Address_____

  _____

  _____

Fees:

- ❏ Day Use $ _____
- ❏ Camp Sites $ _____
- ❏ RV Sites $ _____
- ❏ Refund policy

  _____

  _____

  _____

Make It Personal

Trip dates: _____ | The weather was: Sunny Cloudy Rainy Stormy Snowy Foggy Warm Cold

Why I went:
_____

_____

How I got there: (circle all that apply)   Plane   Train   Car   Bus   Bike   Hike   RV   MC
_____

I went with:
_____

We stayed in (space, cabin # etc):
_____

Most relaxing day:
_____

_____

Something funny:
_____

_____

Someone we met:
_____

_____

Best story told:
_____

_____

The kids liked this:
_____

_____

The best food:
_____

_____

Games played:
_____

_____

Something disappointing:
_____

_____

Next time I'll do this differently:
_____

_____

Bowman Lake State Park
City: Oxford   County: Chenango

Plan your trip: https://parks.ny.gov/parks/bowman/details.aspx

Activities:

- ❑ Biking
- ❑ Boating
- ❑ Canoeing
- ❑ Disc Golf
- ❑ Fishing / Ice
- ❑ Hiking
- ❑ Horseback Riding
- ❑ Hunting
- ❑ Kayaking
- ❑ Marina
- ❑ Nature Center / Trails
- ❑ Photography
- ❑ Playing Fields
- ❑ Scenic Views
- ❑ Swimming
- ❑ Waterfalls
- ❑ Wildlife & Birding
- ❑ Winter Sports
- ❑
- ❑
- ❑
- ❑

Facilities:

- ❑ ADA
- ❑ Picnic sites
- ❑ Restrooms
- ❑ Showers
- ❑ Trailer Access
- ❑ Visitor center
- ❑ Group Camping
- ❑ RV Camp
- ❑ Rustic Camping
- ❑ Cabins / Yurts
- ❑ Day Use Area
- ❑

Notes:

Get the Facts

- ❑ Phone   (607) 334-2718
- ❑ Park Hours

  _____

- ❑ Reservations? _____Y _____N

  date made_____

- ❑ Open all year _____Y_____N

  dates_____

- ❑ Check in time _____
- ❑ Check out time _____
- ❑ Pet friendly _____Y _____N
- ❑ Max RV length _____
- ❑ Distance from home

  miles: _____

  hours: _____

- ❑ Address_____

  _____

  _____

Fees:

- ❑ Day Use $ _____
- ❑ Camp Sites $ _____
- ❑ RV Sites $ _____
- ❑ Refund policy

  _____

  _____

  _____

Make It Personal

Trip dates: _____ | The weather was: Sunny Cloudy Rainy Stormy Snowy Foggy Warm Cold

Why I went:
_____

_____

How I got there: (circle all that apply)   Plane   Train   Car   Bus   Bike   Hike   RV   MC
_____

I went with:
_____

We stayed in (space, cabin # etc):
_____

Most relaxing day:
_____

_____

Something funny:
_____

_____

Someone we met:
_____

_____

Best story told:
_____

_____

The kids liked this:
_____

_____

The best food:
_____

_____

Games played:
_____

_____

Something disappointing:
_____

_____

Next time I'll do this differently:
_____

_____

Delta Lake State Park
City: Rome   County: Oneida

Plan your trip: https://parks.ny.gov/parks/deltalake/details.aspx

Activities:

- ❑ Biking
- ❑ Boating
- ❑ Canoeing
- ❑ Disc Golf
- ❑ Fishing / Ice
- ❑ Hiking
- ❑ Horseback Riding
- ❑ Hunting
- ❑ Kayaking
- ❑ Marina
- ❑ Nature Center / Trails

- ❑ Photography
- ❑ Playing Fields
- ❑ Scenic Views
- ❑ Swimming
- ❑ Waterfalls
- ❑ Wildlife & Birding
- ❑ Winter Sports
- ❑
- ❑
- ❑
- ❑

Facilities:

- ❑ ADA
- ❑ Picnic sites
- ❑ Restrooms
- ❑ Showers
- ❑ Trailer Access
- ❑ Visitor center

- ❑ Group Camping
- ❑ RV Camp
- ❑ Rustic Camping
- ❑ Cabins / Yurts
- ❑ Day Use Area
- ❑

Notes:

Get the Facts

- ❑ Phone   (315) 337-4670
- ❑ Park Hours

  _____

- ❑ Reservations? ____Y ____N

  date made_____

- ❑ Open all year ____Y____N

  dates_____

- ❑ Check in time _____
- ❑ Check out time _____
- ❑ Pet friendly _____Y _____N
- ❑ Max RV length _____
- ❑ Distance from home

  miles: _____

  hours: _____

- ❑ Address_____

  _____

  _____

Fees:

- ❑ Day Use $ _____
- ❑ Camp Sites $ _____
- ❑ RV Sites $ _____
- ❑ Refund policy

  _____

  _____

  _____

Make It Personal

Trip dates: _____ | The weather was: Sunny Cloudy Rainy Stormy Snowy Foggy Warm Cold

Why I went: _____

_____

How I got there: (circle all that apply) Plane Train Car Bus Bike Hike RV MC

I went with: _____

We stayed in (space, cabin # etc): _____

Most relaxing day: _____

_____

Something funny: _____

_____

Someone we met: _____

_____

Best story told: _____

_____

The kids liked this: _____

_____

The best food: _____

_____

Games played: _____

_____

Something disappointing: _____

_____

Next time I'll do this differently: _____

_____

Verona Beach State Park
City: Verona Beach   County: Oneida

Plan your trip: https://parks.ny.gov/parks/veronabeach/details.aspx

Activities:

- ❑ Biking
- ❑ Boating
- ❑ Canoeing
- ❑ Disc Golf
- ❑ Fishing / Ice
- ❑ Hiking
- ❑ Horseback Riding
- ❑ Hunting
- ❑ Kayaking
- ❑ Marina
- ❑ Nature Center / Trails

- ❑ Photography
- ❑ Playing Fields
- ❑ Scenic Views
- ❑ Swimming
- ❑ Waterfalls
- ❑ Wildlife & Birding
- ❑ Winter Sports
- ❑
- ❑
- ❑
- ❑

Facilities:

- ❑ ADA
- ❑ Picnic sites
- ❑ Restrooms
- ❑ Showers
- ❑ Trailer Access
- ❑ Visitor center

- ❑ Group Camping
- ❑ RV Camp
- ❑ Rustic Camping
- ❑ Cabins / Yurts
- ❑ Day Use Area
- ❑

Notes:

Get the Facts

- ❑ Phone   (315) 762-4463
- ❑ Park Hours

  _____

- ❑ Reservations? ____Y ____N

  date made_____

- ❑ Open all year ____Y_____N

  dates_____

- ❑ Check in time _____
- ❑ Check out time _____
- ❑ Pet friendly _____Y _____N
- ❑ Max RV length _____
- ❑ Distance from home

  miles: _____

  hours: _____

- ❑ Address_____

  _____

  _____

Fees:

- ❑ Day Use $ _____
- ❑ Camp Sites $ _____
- ❑ RV Sites $ _____
- ❑ Refund policy

  _____

  _____

  _____

Make It Personal

Trip dates: _____ | The weather was: Sunny Cloudy Rainy Stormy Snowy Foggy Warm Cold

Why I went:
_____
_____

How I got there: (circle all that apply) Plane   Train   Car   Bus   Bike   Hike   RV   MC
_____

I went with:
_____

We stayed in (space, cabin # etc):
_____

Most relaxing day:
_____
_____

Something funny:
_____
_____

Someone we met:
_____
_____

Best story told:
_____
_____

The kids liked this:
_____
_____

The best food:
_____
_____

Games played:
_____
_____

Something disappointing:
_____
_____

Next time I'll do this differently:
_____
_____

Green Lakes State Park
City: Fayetteville   County: Onondaga

Plan your trip: https://parks.ny.gov/parks/greenlakes/details.aspx

Activities:

- ❑ Biking
- ❑ Boating
- ❑ Canoeing
- ❑ Disc Golf
- ❑ Fishing / Ice
- ❑ Hiking
- ❑ Horseback Riding
- ❑ Hunting
- ❑ Kayaking
- ❑ Marina
- ❑ Nature Center / Trails

- ❑ Photography
- ❑ Playing Fields
- ❑ Scenic Views
- ❑ Swimming
- ❑ Waterfalls
- ❑ Wildlife & Birding
- ❑ Winter Sports
- ❑
- ❑
- ❑
- ❑

Facilities:

- ❑ ADA
- ❑ Picnic sites
- ❑ Restrooms
- ❑ Showers
- ❑ Trailer Access
- ❑ Visitor center

- ❑ Group Camping
- ❑ RV Camp
- ❑ Rustic Camping
- ❑ Cabins / Yurts
- ❑ Day Use Area
- ❑

Notes:

Get the Facts

- ❑ Phone   (315) 637-6111
- ❑ Park Hours

  _____

- ❑ Reservations? ____Y ____N

  date made_____

- ❑ Open all year ____Y____N

  dates_____

- ❑ Check in time _____
- ❑ Check out time _____
- ❑ Pet friendly _____Y ____N
- ❑ Max RV length _____
- ❑ Distance from home

  miles: _____

  hours: _____

- ❑ Address_____

  _____

  _____

Fees:

- ❑ Day Use $ _____
- ❑ Camp Sites $ _____
- ❑ RV Sites $ _____
- ❑ Refund policy

  _____

  _____

  _____

Make It Personal

Trip dates: _____ | The weather was: Sunny Cloudy Rainy Stormy Snowy Foggy Warm Cold

Why I went: _____

_____

How I got there: (circle all that apply)   Plane   Train   Car   Bus   Bike   Hike   RV   MC

I went with: _____

We stayed in (space, cabin # etc): _____

Most relaxing day: _____

_____

Something funny: _____

_____

Someone we met: _____

_____

Best story told: _____

_____

The kids liked this: _____

_____

The best food: _____

_____

Games played: _____

_____

Something disappointing: _____

_____

Next time I'll do this differently: _____

_____

Selkirk Shores State Park

City: Pulaski **County: Oswego**

Plan your trip: https://parks.ny.gov/parks/selkirkshores/details.aspx

Activities:

- ❑ Biking
- ❑ Boating
- ❑ Canoeing
- ❑ Disc Golf
- ❑ Fishing / Ice
- ❑ Hiking
- ❑ Horseback Riding
- ❑ Hunting
- ❑ Kayaking
- ❑ Marina
- ❑ Nature Center / Trails

- ❑ Photography
- ❑ Playing Fields
- ❑ Scenic Views
- ❑ Swimming
- ❑ Waterfalls
- ❑ Wildlife & Birding
- ❑ Winter Sports
- ❑
- ❑
- ❑
- ❑

Facilities:

- ❑ ADA
- ❑ Picnic sites
- ❑ Restrooms
- ❑ Showers
- ❑ Trailer Access
- ❑ Visitor center

- ❑ Group Camping
- ❑ RV Camp
- ❑ Rustic Camping
- ❑ Cabins / Yurts
- ❑ Day Use Area
- ❑

Notes:

Get the Facts

- ❑ Phone   (315) 298-5737
- ❑ Park Hours

  _____

- ❑ Reservations? _____Y _____N

  date made_____
- ❑ Open all year _____Y_____N

  dates_____
- ❑ Check in time _____
- ❑ Check out time _____
- ❑ Pet friendly _____Y _____N
- ❑ Max RV length _____
- ❑ Distance from home

  miles: _____

  hours: _____
- ❑ Address_____

  _____

  _____

Fees:

- ❑ Day Use $ _____
- ❑ Camp Sites $ _____
- ❑ RV Sites $ _____
- ❑ Refund policy

  _____

  _____

  _____

Make It Personal

Trip dates: _____ | The weather was: Sunny Cloudy Rainy Stormy Snowy Foggy Warm Cold

Why I went:
_____
_____

How I got there: (circle all that apply)   Plane   Train   Car   Bus   Bike   Hike   RV   MC
_____

I went with:
_____

We stayed in (space, cabin # etc):
_____

Most relaxing day:
_____
_____

Something funny:
_____
_____

Someone we met:
_____
_____

Best story told:
_____
_____

The kids liked this:
_____
_____

The best food:
_____
_____

Games played:
_____
_____

Something disappointing:
_____
_____

Next time I'll do this differently:
_____
_____

Glimmerglass State Park
City: Cooperstown   County: Otsego

Plan your trip: https://parks.ny.gov/parks/glimmerglass/details.aspx

Activities:

- ❑ Biking
- ❑ Boating
- ❑ Canoeing
- ❑ Disc Golf
- ❑ Fishing / Ice
- ❑ Hiking
- ❑ Horseback Riding
- ❑ Hunting
- ❑ Kayaking
- ❑ Marina
- ❑ Nature Center / Trails

- ❑ Photography
- ❑ Playing Fields
- ❑ Scenic Views
- ❑ Swimming
- ❑ Waterfalls
- ❑ Wildlife & Birding
- ❑ Winter Sports
- ❑
- ❑
- ❑
- ❑

Facilities:

- ❑ ADA
- ❑ Picnic sites
- ❑ Restrooms
- ❑ Showers
- ❑ Trailer Access
- ❑ Visitor center

- ❑ Group Camping
- ❑ RV Camp
- ❑ Rustic Camping
- ❑ Cabins / Yurts
- ❑ Day Use Area
- ❑

Notes:

Get the Facts

- ❑ Phone   (607) 547-8662
- ❑ Park Hours

  _____

- ❑ Reservations? ____Y ____N

  date made_____

- ❑ Open all year ____Y_____N

  dates_____

- ❑ Check in time _____
- ❑ Check out time _____
- ❑ Pet friendly _____Y _____N
- ❑ Max RV length _____
- ❑ Distance from home

  miles: _____

  hours: _____

- ❑ Address_____

  _____

  _____

Fees:

- ❑ Day Use $ _____
- ❑ Camp Sites $ _____
- ❑ RV Sites $ _____
- ❑ Refund policy

  _____

  _____

  _____

Make It Personal

Trip dates: _____ | The weather was: Sunny Cloudy Rainy Stormy Snowy Foggy Warm Cold

Why I went: _____
_____

How I got there: (circle all that apply)   Plane   Train   Car   Bus   Bike   Hike   RV   MC
_____

I went with: _____

We stayed in (space, cabin # etc): _____

Most relaxing day: _____
_____

Something funny: _____
_____

Someone we met: _____
_____

Best story told: _____
_____

The kids liked this: _____
_____

The best food: _____
_____

Games played: _____
_____

Something disappointing: _____
_____

Next time I'll do this differently: _____
_____

Gilbert Lake State Park
City: Laurens   County: Otsego

Plan your trip: https://parks.ny.gov/parks/gilbertlake/details.aspx

Activities:

- ❏ Biking
- ❏ Boating
- ❏ Canoeing
- ❏ Disc Golf
- ❏ Fishing / Ice
- ❏ Hiking
- ❏ Horseback Riding
- ❏ Hunting
- ❏ Kayaking
- ❏ Marina
- ❏ Nature Center / Trails
- ❏ Photography
- ❏ Playing Fields
- ❏ Scenic Views
- ❏ Swimming
- ❏ Waterfalls
- ❏ Wildlife & Birding
- ❏ Winter Sports
- ❏
- ❏
- ❏
- ❏

Facilities:

- ❏ ADA
- ❏ Picnic sites
- ❏ Restrooms
- ❏ Showers
- ❏ Trailer Access
- ❏ Visitor center
- ❏ Group Camping
- ❏ RV Camp
- ❏ Rustic Camping
- ❏ Cabins / Yurts
- ❏ Day Use Area
- ❏

Notes:

Get the Facts

- ❏ Phone   (607) 432-2114
- ❏ Park Hours

  _____

- ❏ Reservations? ____Y ____N

  date made_____

- ❏ Open all year ____Y_____N

  dates_____

- ❏ Check in time _____
- ❏ Check out time _____
- ❏ Pet friendly _____Y _____N
- ❏ Max RV length _____
- ❏ Distance from home

  miles: _____

  hours: _____

- ❏ Address_____

  _____

  _____

Fees:

- ❏ Day Use $ _____
- ❏ Camp Sites $ _____
- ❏ RV Sites $ _____
- ❏ Refund policy

  _____

  _____

  _____

Make It Personal

Trip dates: _____ | The weather was: Sunny Cloudy Rainy Stormy Snowy Foggy Warm Cold

Why I went: _____

_____

How I got there: (circle all that apply) Plane Train Car Bus Bike Hike RV MC

I went with: _____

We stayed in (space, cabin # etc): _____

Most relaxing day: _____

_____

Something funny: _____

_____

Someone we met: _____

_____

Best story told: _____

_____

The kids liked this: _____

_____

The best food: _____

_____

Games played: _____

_____

Something disappointing: _____

_____

Next time I'll do this differently: _____

_____

Betty and Wilbur Davis State Park
City: Schenevus   County: Otsego

Plan your trip: https://parks.ny.gov/parks/bettywilburdavis/details.aspx

Activities:

- ☐ Biking
- ☐ Boating
- ☐ Canoeing
- ☐ Disc Golf
- ☐ Fishing / Ice
- ☐ Hiking
- ☐ Horseback Riding
- ☐ Hunting
- ☐ Kayaking
- ☐ Marina
- ☐ Nature Center / Trails

- ☐ Photography
- ☐ Playing Fields
- ☐ Scenic Views
- ☐ Swimming
- ☐ Waterfalls
- ☐ Wildlife & Birding
- ☐ Winter Sports
- ☐
- ☐
- ☐
- ☐

Facilities:

- ☐ ADA
- ☐ Picnic sites
- ☐ Restrooms
- ☐ Showers
- ☐ Trailer Access
- ☐ Visitor center

- ☐ Group Camping
- ☐ RV Camp
- ☐ Rustic Camping
- ☐ Cabins / Yurts
- ☐ Day Use Area
- ☐

Notes:

Get the Facts

- ☐ Phone   (607) 547-8662
- ☐ Park Hours

_____

- ☐ Reservations? ____Y ____N

date made_____

- ☐ Open all year ____Y ____N

dates_____

- ☐ Check in time _____
- ☐ Check out time _____
- ☐ Pet friendly _____Y _____N
- ☐ Max RV length _____
- ☐ Distance from home

miles: _____

hours: _____

- ☐ Address_____

_____

_____

Fees:

- ☐ Day Use $ _____
- ☐ Camp Sites $ _____
- ☐ RV Sites $ _____
- ☐ Refund policy

_____

_____

_____

Make It Personal

Trip dates: _____ | The weather was: Sunny Cloudy Rainy Stormy Snowy Foggy Warm Cold

Why I went:

_____

_____

How I got there: (circle all that apply)   Plane   Train   Car   Bus   Bike   Hike   RV   MC

_____

I went with:

_____

We stayed in (space, cabin # etc):

_____

Most relaxing day:

_____

_____

Something funny:

_____

_____

Someone we met:

_____

_____

Best story told:

_____

_____

The kids liked this:

_____

_____

The best food:

_____

_____

Games played:

_____

_____

Something disappointing:

_____

_____

Next time I'll do this differently:

_____

_____

Robert V. Riddell State Park
City: Davenport   County: Delaware

Plan your trip: https://parks.ny.gov/parks/robertriddell/details.aspx

Activities: (check all that apply)

- ❑ Beach
- ❑ Biking
- ❑ Boating
- ❑ Canoeing
- ❑ Fishing / Ice
- ❑ Hiking
- ❑ Horseback Riding
- ❑ Hunting
- ❑ Kayaking

- ❑ Marina
- ❑ Nature Center
- ❑ Photography
- ❑ Swimming
- ❑ Waterfalls
- ❑ Watersports
- ❑ Wildlife & Birding
- ❑ Winter Sports
- ❑

Facilities:

- ❑ ADA
- ❑ Gift Shop
- ❑ Museum
- ❑ Visitor Center
- ❑ Restrooms

- ❑ Playground
- ❑ Picnic sites
- ❑
- ❑
- ❑

Memories of the Trip

Get the Facts

- ❑ Phone   (607) 432-2114
- ❑ Park Hours

  _____

- ❑ Reservations? _____Y _____N

  date made_____

- ❑ Open all year? _____Y_____N

  dates_____

- ❑ Dog friendly _____Y _____N
- ❑ Distance from home

  miles: _____

  hours: _____

- ❑ Address_____

  _____

  _____

Fees:

- ❑ Day Use $ _____
- ❑ Refund policy

  _____

  _____

  _____

Stamps & Stickers

Chittenango Falls State Park
City: Cazenovia   County: Madison

Plan your trip: https://parks.ny.gov/parks/chittenangofalls/details.aspx

Activities: (check all that apply)

- ❑ Beach
- ❑ Biking
- ❑ Boating
- ❑ Canoeing
- ❑ Fishing / Ice
- ❑ Hiking
- ❑ Horseback Riding
- ❑ Hunting
- ❑ Kayaking

- ❑ Marina
- ❑ Nature Center
- ❑ Photography
- ❑ Swimming
- ❑ Waterfalls
- ❑ Watersports
- ❑ Wildlife & Birding
- ❑ Winter Sports
- ❑

Facilities:

- ❑ ADA
- ❑ Gift Shop
- ❑ Museum
- ❑ Visitor Center
- ❑ Restrooms

- ❑ Playground
- ❑ Picnic sites
- ❑
- ❑
- ❑

Get the Facts

- ❑ Phone   (315) 492-1756
- ❑ Park Hours

  _____

- ❑ Reservations? ____ Y ____ N

  date made_____

- ❑ Open all year? ____ Y ____ N

  dates_____

- ❑ Dog friendly _____ Y _____ N

- ❑ Distance from home

  miles: _____

  hours: _____

- ❑ Address_____

  _____

  _____

Fees:

- ❑ Day Use $ _____
- ❑ Refund policy

  _____

  _____

  _____

Memories of the Trip

Stamps & Stickers

Helen McNitt State Park
City: Cazenovia County: Madison

Plan your trip: https://parks.ny.gov/parks/helenmcnitt/details.aspx

Activities: (check all that apply)

- ❑ Beach
- ❑ Biking
- ❑ Boating
- ❑ Canoeing
- ❑ Fishing / Ice
- ❑ Hiking
- ❑ Horseback Riding
- ❑ Hunting
- ❑ Kayaking

- ❑ Marina
- ❑ Nature Center
- ❑ Photography
- ❑ Swimming
- ❑ Waterfalls
- ❑ Watersports
- ❑ Wildlife & Birding
- ❑ Winter Sports
- ❑

Facilities:

- ❑ ADA
- ❑ Gift Shop
- ❑ Museum
- ❑ Visitor Center
- ❑ Restrooms

- ❑ Playground
- ❑ Picnic sites
- ❑
- ❑
- ❑

Memories of the Trip

Get the Facts

- ❑ Phone   (315) 492-1756
- ❑ Park Hours

  _____

- ❑ Reservations? ____Y ____N

  date made_____

- ❑ Open all year? ____Y____N

  dates_____

- ❑ Dog friendly _____Y _____N

- ❑ Distance from home

  miles: _____

  hours: _____

- ❑ Address_____

  _____

  _____

Fees:

- ❑ Day Use $ _____
- ❑ Refund policy

  _____

  _____

  _____

Stamps & Stickers

Pixley Falls State Park
City: Boonville   County: Oneida

Plan your trip: https://parks.ny.gov/parks/pixleyfalls/details.aspx

Activities: (check all that apply)

- ☐ Beach
- ☐ Biking
- ☐ Boating
- ☐ Canoeing
- ☐ Fishing / Ice
- ☐ Hiking
- ☐ Horseback Riding
- ☐ Hunting
- ☐ Kayaking

- ☐ Marina
- ☐ Nature Center
- ☐ Photography
- ☐ Swimming
- ☐ Waterfalls
- ☐ Watersports
- ☐ Wildlife & Birding
- ☐ Winter Sports
- ☐

Facilities:

- ☐ ADA
- ☐ Gift Shop
- ☐ Museum
- ☐ Visitor Center
- ☐ Restrooms

- ☐ Playground
- ☐ Picnic sites
- ☐
- ☐
- ☐

Memories of the Trip

Get the Facts

- ☐ Phone   (315) 337-4670
- ☐ Park Hours

  _____

- ☐ Reservations? ____Y ____N

  date made_____

- ☐ Open all year? ____Y____N

  dates_____

- ☐ Dog friendly _____Y _____N
- ☐ Distance from home

  miles: _____

  hours: _____

- ☐ Address_____

  _____

  _____

Fees:

- ☐ Day Use $ _____
- ☐ Refund policy

  _____

  _____

  _____

Stamps & Stickers

Clark Reservation State Park

City: Jamesville   **County: Onondaga**

Plan your trip: https://parks.ny.gov/parks/clarkreservation/details.aspx

Activities: (check all that apply)

- ❑ Beach
- ❑ Biking
- ❑ Boating
- ❑ Canoeing
- ❑ Fishing / Ice
- ❑ Hiking
- ❑ Horseback Riding
- ❑ Hunting
- ❑ Kayaking

- ❑ Marina
- ❑ Nature Center
- ❑ Photography
- ❑ Swimming
- ❑ Waterfalls
- ❑ Watersports
- ❑ Wildlife & Birding
- ❑ Winter Sports
- ❑

Facilities:

- ❑ ADA
- ❑ Gift Shop
- ❑ Museum
- ❑ Visitor Center
- ❑ Restrooms

- ❑ Playground
- ❑ Picnic sites
- ❑
- ❑
- ❑

Memories of the Trip

Get the Facts

- ❑ Phone   (315) 492-1756
- ❑ Park Hours

  _____

- ❑ Reservations? _____Y _____N

  date made_____

- ❑ Open all year? _____Y_____N

  dates_____

- ❑ Dog friendly _____Y _____N

- ❑ Distance from home

  miles: _____

  hours: _____

- ❑ Address_____

  _____

  _____

Fees:

- ❑ Day Use $ _____
- ❑ Refund policy

  _____

  _____

  _____

Stamps & Stickers

State Park at the Fair

City: Syracuse   **County: Onondaga**

Plan your trip: https://parks.ny.gov/parks/statefair/details.aspx

Activities: (check all that apply)

- ❑ Beach
- ❑ Biking
- ❑ Boating
- ❑ Canoeing
- ❑ Fishing / Ice
- ❑ Hiking
- ❑ Horseback Riding
- ❑ Hunting
- ❑ Kayaking

- ❑ Marina
- ❑ Nature Center
- ❑ Photography
- ❑ Swimming
- ❑ Waterfalls
- ❑ Watersports
- ❑ Wildlife & Birding
- ❑ Winter Sports
- ❑

Facilities:

- ❑ ADA
- ❑ Gift Shop
- ❑ Museum
- ❑ Visitor Center
- ❑ Restrooms

- ❑ Playground
- ❑ Picnic sites
- ❑
- ❑
- ❑

Memories of the Trip

Get the Facts

- ❑ Phone   (315) 492-1756
- ❑ Park Hours

  _____

- ❑ Reservations? ____Y ____N

  date made_____

- ❑ Open all year? ____Y____N

  dates_____

- ❑ Dog friendly _____Y _____N

- ❑ Distance from home

  miles: _____

  hours: _____

- ❑ Address_____

  _____

  _____

Fees:

- ❑ Day Use $ _____
- ❑ Refund policy

  _____

  _____

  _____

Stamps & Stickers

Battle Island State Park
City: Fulton   County: Oswego

Plan your trip: https://parks.ny.gov/parks/battleisland/details.aspx

Activities: (check all that apply)

- ❑ Beach
- ❑ Biking
- ❑ Boating
- ❑ Canoeing
- ❑ Fishing / Ice
- ❑ Hiking
- ❑ Horseback Riding
- ❑ Hunting
- ❑ Kayaking

- ❑ Marina
- ❑ Nature Center
- ❑ Photography
- ❑ Swimming
- ❑ Waterfalls
- ❑ Watersports
- ❑ Wildlife & Birding
- ❑ Winter Sports
- ❑

Facilities:

- ❑ ADA
- ❑ Gift Shop
- ❑ Museum
- ❑ Visitor Center
- ❑ Restrooms

- ❑ Playground
- ❑ Picnic sites
- ❑
- ❑
- ❑

Memories of the Trip

Get the Facts

- ❑ Phone   (315) 593-3408
- ❑ Park Hours

  _____

- ❑ Reservations? _____ Y _____ N

  date made_____

- ❑ Open all year? _____ Y _____ N

  dates_____

- ❑ Dog friendly _____ Y _____ N

- ❑ Distance from home

  miles: _____

  hours: _____

- ❑ Address_____

  _____

  _____

Fees:

- ❑ Day Use $ _____
- ❑ Refund policy

  _____

  _____

  _____

Stamps & Stickers

Sandy Island Beach State Park
City: Pulaski   County: Oswego

Plan your trip: https://parks.ny.gov/parks/sandyisland/details.aspx

Activities: (check all that apply)

- ❑ Beach
- ❑ Biking
- ❑ Boating
- ❑ Canoeing
- ❑ Fishing / Ice
- ❑ Hiking
- ❑ Horseback Riding
- ❑ Hunting
- ❑ Kayaking

- ❑ Marina
- ❑ Nature Center
- ❑ Photography
- ❑ Swimming
- ❑ Waterfalls
- ❑ Watersports
- ❑ Wildlife & Birding
- ❑ Winter Sports
- ❑

Facilities:

- ❑ ADA
- ❑ Gift Shop
- ❑ Museum
- ❑ Visitor Center
- ❑ Restrooms

- ❑ Playground
- ❑ Picnic sites
- ❑
- ❑
- ❑

Memories of the Trip

Get the Facts

- ❑ Phone   (315) 387-2657
- ❑ Park Hours

  _____

- ❑ Reservations? _____Y _____N

  date made_____

- ❑ Open all year? _____Y_____N

  dates_____

- ❑ Dog friendly _____Y _____N

- ❑ Distance from home

  miles: _____

  hours: _____

- ❑ Address_____

  _____

  _____

Fees:

- ❑ Day Use $ _____
- ❑ Refund policy

  _____

  _____

  _____

Stamps & Stickers

Canadarago State Marine Park
City: Richfield Springs   County: Otsego

Plan your trip: https://parks.ny.gov/parks/Canadarago/details.aspx

Activities: (check all that apply)

- ❑ Beach
- ❑ Biking
- ❑ Boating
- ❑ Canoeing
- ❑ Fishing / Ice
- ❑ Hiking
- ❑ Horseback Riding
- ❑ Hunting
- ❑ Kayaking

- ❑ Marina
- ❑ Nature Center
- ❑ Photography
- ❑ Swimming
- ❑ Waterfalls
- ❑ Watersports
- ❑ Wildlife & Birding
- ❑ Winter Sports
- ❑

Facilities:

- ❑ ADA
- ❑ Gift Shop
- ❑ Museum
- ❑ Visitor Center
- ❑ Restrooms

- ❑ Playground
- ❑ Picnic sites
- ❑
- ❑
- ❑

Memories of the Trip

Get the Facts

- ❑ Phone   (607) 547-8662
- ❑ Park Hours

_____

- ❑ Reservations? ____Y ____N

date made_____

- ❑ Open all year? ____Y____N

dates_____

- ❑ Dog friendly _____Y _____N
- ❑ Distance from home

miles: _____

hours: _____

- ❑ Address_____

_____

_____

Fees:

- ❑ Day Use $ _____
- ❑ Refund policy

_____

_____

_____

Stamps & Stickers

Saratoga & Capital District Region

- Albany County
- Greene County
- Rensselaer County
- Saratoga County
- Schoharie County

Thompson's Lake Campground-Thacher State Park

City: East Berne   County: Albany

Plan your trip: https://parks.ny.gov/parks/thompsonslake/details.aspx

Activities:

- ☐ Biking
- ☐ Boating
- ☐ Canoeing
- ☐ Disc Golf
- ☐ Fishing / Ice
- ☐ Hiking
- ☐ Horseback Riding
- ☐ Hunting
- ☐ Kayaking
- ☐ Marina
- ☐ Nature Center / Trails
- ☐ Photography
- ☐ Playing Fields
- ☐ Scenic Views
- ☐ Swimming
- ☐ Waterfalls
- ☐ Wildlife & Birding
- ☐ Winter Sports
- ☐
- ☐
- ☐
- ☐

Facilities:

- ☐ ADA
- ☐ Picnic sites
- ☐ Restrooms
- ☐ Showers
- ☐ Trailer Access
- ☐ Visitor center
- ☐ Group Camping
- ☐ RV Camp
- ☐ Rustic Camping
- ☐ Cabins / Yurts
- ☐ Day Use Area
- ☐

Notes:

Get the Facts

- ☐ Phone   (518) 872-1674
- ☐ Park Hours

  _____

- ☐ Reservations? ____Y ____N

  date made_____
- ☐ Open all year ____Y_____N

  dates_____
- ☐ Check in time _____
- ☐ Check out time _____
- ☐ Pet friendly _____Y _____N
- ☐ Max RV length _____
- ☐ Distance from home

  miles: _____

  hours: _____
- ☐ Address_____

  _____

  _____

Fees:

- ☐ Day Use $ _____
- ☐ Camp Sites $ _____
- ☐ RV Sites $ _____
- ☐ Refund policy

  _____

  _____

  _____

Make It Personal

Trip dates: _____

The weather was: Sunny Cloudy Rainy Stormy Snowy Foggy Warm Cold

Why I went:
_____

How I got there: (circle all that apply) Plane Train Car Bus Bike Hike RV MC

I went with:
_____

We stayed in (space, cabin # etc):
_____

Most relaxing day:
_____

Something funny:
_____

Someone we met:
_____

Best story told:
_____

The kids liked this:
_____

The best food:
_____

Games played:
_____

Something disappointing:
_____

Next time I'll do this differently:
_____
_____

Thacher State Park
City: Voorheesville   County: Albany

Plan your trip: https://parks.ny.gov/parks/thacher/details.aspx

Activities:

- ☐ Biking
- ☐ Boating
- ☐ Canoeing
- ☐ Disc Golf
- ☐ Fishing / Ice
- ☐ Hiking
- ☐ Horseback Riding
- ☐ Hunting
- ☐ Kayaking
- ☐ Marina
- ☐ Nature Center / Trails
- ☐ Photography
- ☐ Playing Fields
- ☐ Scenic Views
- ☐ Swimming
- ☐ Waterfalls
- ☐ Wildlife & Birding
- ☐ Winter Sports
- ☐
- ☐
- ☐
- ☐

Facilities:

- ☐ ADA
- ☐ Picnic sites
- ☐ Restrooms
- ☐ Showers
- ☐ Trailer Access
- ☐ Visitor center
- ☐ Group Camping
- ☐ RV Camp
- ☐ Rustic Camping
- ☐ Cabins / Yurts
- ☐ Day Use Area
- ☐

Notes:

Get the Facts

- ☐ Phone   (518) 872-1237
- ☐ Park Hours

_____

- ☐ Reservations? _____Y _____N

date made_____

- ☐ Open all year _____Y_____N

dates_____

- ☐ Check in time _____
- ☐ Check out time _____
- ☐ Pet friendly _____Y _____N
- ☐ Max RV length _____
- ☐ Distance from home

miles: _____

hours: _____

- ☐ Address_____

_____

_____

Fees:

- ☐ Day Use $ _____
- ☐ Camp Sites $ _____
- ☐ RV Sites $ _____
- ☐ Refund policy

_____

_____

_____

Make It Personal

Trip dates: _____ | The weather was: Sunny Cloudy Rainy Stormy Snowy Foggy Warm Cold

Why I went:
_____
_____

How I got there: (circle all that apply)   Plane   Train   Car   Bus   Bike   Hike   RV   MC
_____

I went with:
_____

We stayed in (space, cabin # etc):
_____

Most relaxing day:
_____
_____

Something funny:
_____
_____

Someone we met:
_____
_____

Best story told:
_____
_____

The kids liked this:
_____
_____

The best food:
_____
_____

Games played:
_____
_____

Something disappointing:
_____
_____

Next time I'll do this differently:
_____
_____

Hudson River Islands State Park
City: Coxsackie   County: Greene

Plan your trip: https://parks.ny.gov/parks/hudsonriverislands/details.aspx

Activities:

- ❑ Biking
- ❑ Boating
- ❑ Canoeing
- ❑ Disc Golf
- ❑ Fishing / Ice
- ❑ Hiking
- ❑ Horseback Riding
- ❑ Hunting
- ❑ Kayaking
- ❑ Marina
- ❑ Nature Center / Trails

- ❑ Photography
- ❑ Playing Fields
- ❑ Scenic Views
- ❑ Swimming
- ❑ Waterfalls
- ❑ Wildlife & Birding
- ❑ Winter Sports
- ❑
- ❑
- ❑
- ❑

Facilities:

- ❑ ADA
- ❑ Picnic sites
- ❑ Restrooms
- ❑ Showers
- ❑ Trailer Access
- ❑ Visitor center

- ❑ Group Camping
- ❑ RV Camp
- ❑ Rustic Camping
- ❑ Cabins / Yurts
- ❑ Day Use Area
- ❑

Notes:

Get the Facts

- ❑ Phone   (518) 732-0187
- ❑ Park Hours

  _____

- ❑ Reservations? ____Y ____N

  date made_____

- ❑ Open all year ____Y____N

  dates_____

- ❑ Check in time _____
- ❑ Check out time _____
- ❑ Pet friendly _____Y _____N
- ❑ Max RV length _____
- ❑ Distance from home

  miles: _____

  hours: _____

- ❑ Address_____

  _____

  _____

Fees:

- ❑ Day Use $ _____
- ❑ Camp Sites $ _____
- ❑ RV Sites $ _____
- ❑ Refund policy

  _____

  _____

  _____

Make It Personal

Trip dates: _____ | The weather was: Sunny Cloudy Rainy Stormy Snowy Foggy Warm Cold

Why I went:
_____

_____

How I got there: (circle all that apply)   Plane   Train   Car   Bus   Bike   Hike   RV   MC
_____

I went with:
_____

We stayed in (space, cabin # etc):
_____

Most relaxing day:
_____

_____

Something funny:
_____

_____

Someone we met:
_____

_____

Best story told:
_____

_____

The kids liked this:
_____

_____

The best food:
_____

_____

Games played:
_____

_____

Something disappointing:
_____

_____

Next time I'll do this differently:
_____

_____

Cherry Plain State Park
City: Petersburg   County: Rensselaer

Plan your trip: https://parks.ny.gov/parks/cherryplain/details.aspx

Activities:

- ❏ Biking
- ❏ Boating
- ❏ Canoeing
- ❏ Disc Golf
- ❏ Fishing / Ice
- ❏ Hiking
- ❏ Horseback Riding
- ❏ Hunting
- ❏ Kayaking
- ❏ Marina
- ❏ Nature Center / Trails
- ❏ Photography
- ❏ Playing Fields
- ❏ Scenic Views
- ❏ Swimming
- ❏ Waterfalls
- ❏ Wildlife & Birding
- ❏ Winter Sports
- ❏
- ❏
- ❏
- ❏

Facilities:

- ❏ ADA
- ❏ Picnic sites
- ❏ Restrooms
- ❏ Showers
- ❏ Trailer Access
- ❏ Visitor center
- ❏ Group Camping
- ❏ RV Camp
- ❏ Rustic Camping
- ❏ Cabins / Yurts
- ❏ Day Use Area
- ❏

Notes:

Get the Facts

- ❏ Phone   (518) 733-5400
- ❏ Park Hours

  _____

- ❏ Reservations? _____Y _____N

  date made_____

- ❏ Open all year _____Y_____N

  dates_____

- ❏ Check in time _____
- ❏ Check out time _____
- ❏ Pet friendly _____Y _____N
- ❏ Max RV length _____
- ❏ Distance from home

  miles: _____

  hours: _____

- ❏ Address_____

  _____

  _____

Fees:

- ❏ Day Use $ _____
- ❏ Camp Sites $ _____
- ❏ RV Sites $ _____
- ❏ Refund policy

  _____

  _____

  _____

Make It Personal

Trip dates: _____ | The weather was: Sunny Cloudy Rainy Stormy Snowy Foggy Warm Cold

Why I went:
_____

_____

How I got there: (circle all that apply)   Plane   Train   Car   Bus   Bike   Hike   RV   MC
_____

I went with:
_____

We stayed in (space, cabin # etc):
_____

Most relaxing day:
_____

_____

Something funny:
_____

_____

Someone we met:
_____

_____

Best story told:
_____

_____

The kids liked this:
_____

_____

The best food:
_____

_____

Games played:
_____

_____

Something disappointing:
_____

_____

Next time I'll do this differently:
_____

_____

Schodack Island State Park
City: Schodack Landing   County: Rensselaer

Plan your trip: https://parks.ny.gov/parks/schodackisland/details.aspx

Activities:

- ❑ Biking
- ❑ Boating
- ❑ Canoeing
- ❑ Disc Golf
- ❑ Fishing / Ice
- ❑ Hiking
- ❑ Horseback Riding
- ❑ Hunting
- ❑ Kayaking
- ❑ Marina
- ❑ Nature Center / Trails

- ❑ Photography
- ❑ Playing Fields
- ❑ Scenic Views
- ❑ Swimming
- ❑ Waterfalls
- ❑ Wildlife & Birding
- ❑ Winter Sports
- ❑
- ❑
- ❑
- ❑

Facilities:

- ❑ ADA
- ❑ Picnic sites
- ❑ Restrooms
- ❑ Showers
- ❑ Trailer Access
- ❑ Visitor center

- ❑ Group Camping
- ❑ RV Camp
- ❑ Rustic Camping
- ❑ Cabins / Yurts
- ❑ Day Use Area
- ❑

Notes:

Get the Facts

- ❑ Phone   (518) 732-0187
- ❑ Park Hours

_____

- ❑ Reservations? _____Y _____N

date made_____

- ❑ Open all year _____Y_____N

dates_____

- ❑ Check in time _____
- ❑ Check out time _____
- ❑ Pet friendly _____Y _____N
- ❑ Max RV length _____
- ❑ Distance from home

miles: _____

hours: _____

- ❑ Address_____

_____

_____

Fees:

- ❑ Day Use $ _____
- ❑ Camp Sites $ _____
- ❑ RV Sites $ _____
- ❑ Refund policy

_____

_____

_____

Make It Personal

Trip dates: _____

The weather was: Sunny Cloudy Rainy Stormy Snowy Foggy Warm Cold

Why I went: _____

_____

How I got there: (circle all that apply) Plane Train Car Bus Bike Hike RV MC

I went with: _____

We stayed in (space, cabin # etc): _____

Most relaxing day: _____

_____

Something funny: _____

_____

Someone we met: _____

_____

Best story told: _____

_____

The kids liked this: _____

_____

The best food: _____

_____

Games played: _____

_____

Something disappointing: _____

_____

Next time I'll do this differently: _____

_____

Moreau Lake State Park

City: Gansevoort   County: Saratoga

Plan your trip: https://parks.ny.gov/parks/moreaulake/details.aspx

Activities:

- ❑ Biking
- ❑ Boating
- ❑ Canoeing
- ❑ Disc Golf
- ❑ Fishing / Ice
- ❑ Hiking
- ❑ Horseback Riding
- ❑ Hunting
- ❑ Kayaking
- ❑ Marina
- ❑ Nature Center / Trails

- ❑ Photography
- ❑ Playing Fields
- ❑ Scenic Views
- ❑ Swimming
- ❑ Waterfalls
- ❑ Wildlife & Birding
- ❑ Winter Sports
- ❑
- ❑
- ❑
- ❑

Facilities:

- ❑ ADA
- ❑ Picnic sites
- ❑ Restrooms
- ❑ Showers
- ❑ Trailer Access
- ❑ Visitor center

- ❑ Group Camping
- ❑ RV Camp
- ❑ Rustic Camping
- ❑ Cabins / Yurts
- ❑ Day Use Area
- ❑

Notes:

Get the Facts

- ❑ Phone   (518) 793-0511
- ❑ Park Hours

  _____

- ❑ Reservations? _____Y _____N

  date made_____

- ❑ Open all year _____Y _____N

  dates_____

- ❑ Check in time _____
- ❑ Check out time _____
- ❑ Pet friendly _____Y _____N
- ❑ Max RV length _____
- ❑ Distance from home

  miles: _____

  hours: _____

- ❑ Address_____

  _____

  _____

Fees:

- ❑ Day Use $ _____
- ❑ Camp Sites $ _____
- ❑ RV Sites $ _____
- ❑ Refund policy

  _____

  _____

  _____

Make It Personal

Trip dates:
_____

The weather was: Sunny Cloudy Rainy Stormy Snowy Foggy Warm Cold

Why I went:
_____

How I got there: (circle all that apply) Plane Train Car Bus Bike Hike RV MC

I went with:
_____

We stayed in (space, cabin # etc):
_____

Most relaxing day:
_____

Something funny:
_____

Someone we met:
_____

Best story told:
_____

The kids liked this:
_____

The best food:
_____

Games played:
_____

Something disappointing:
_____

Next time I'll do this differently:
_____

Max V. Shaul State Park
City: Fultonham   County: Schoharie

Plan your trip: https://parks.ny.gov/parks/maxvshaul/details.aspx

Activities:

- ☐ Biking
- ☐ Boating
- ☐ Canoeing
- ☐ Disc Golf
- ☐ Fishing / Ice
- ☐ Hiking
- ☐ Horseback Riding
- ☐ Hunting
- ☐ Kayaking
- ☐ Marina
- ☐ Nature Center / Trails

- ☐ Photography
- ☐ Playing Fields
- ☐ Scenic Views
- ☐ Swimming
- ☐ Waterfalls
- ☐ Wildlife & Birding
- ☐ Winter Sports
- ☐
- ☐
- ☐
- ☐

Facilities:

- ☐ ADA
- ☐ Picnic sites
- ☐ Restrooms
- ☐ Showers
- ☐ Trailer Access
- ☐ Visitor center

- ☐ Group Camping
- ☐ RV Camp
- ☐ Rustic Camping
- ☐ Cabins / Yurts
- ☐ Day Use Area
- ☐

Notes:

Get the Facts

- ☐ Phone   (518) 827-4711
- ☐ Park Hours

  _____

- ☐ Reservations? ____Y ____N

  date made_____

- ☐ Open all year ____Y____N

  dates_____

- ☐ Check in time _____
- ☐ Check out time _____
- ☐ Pet friendly _____Y _____N
- ☐ Max RV length _____
- ☐ Distance from home

  miles: _____

  hours: _____

- ☐ Address_____

  _____

  _____

Fees:

- ☐ Day Use $ _____
- ☐ Camp Sites $ _____
- ☐ RV Sites $ _____
- ☐ Refund policy

  _____

  _____

  _____

Make It Personal

Trip dates: _____ | The weather was: Sunny Cloudy Rainy Stormy Snowy Foggy Warm Cold

Why I went:
_____

How I got there: (circle all that apply)   Plane   Train   Car   Bus   Bike   Hike   RV   MC
_____

I went with:
_____

We stayed in (space, cabin # etc):
_____

Most relaxing day:
_____

Something funny:
_____

Someone we met:
_____

Best story told:
_____

The kids liked this:
_____

The best food:
_____

Games played:
_____

Something disappointing:
_____

Next time I'll do this differently:
_____

Peebles Island State Park
City: Cohoes   County: Albany

Plan your trip: https://parks.ny.gov/parks/peeblesisland/details.aspx

Activities: (check all that apply)

- ❑ Beach
- ❑ Biking
- ❑ Boating
- ❑ Canoeing
- ❑ Fishing / Ice
- ❑ Hiking
- ❑ Horseback Riding
- ❑ Hunting
- ❑ Kayaking

- ❑ Marina
- ❑ Nature Center
- ❑ Photography
- ❑ Swimming
- ❑ Waterfalls
- ❑ Watersports
- ❑ Wildlife & Birding
- ❑ Winter Sports
- ❑

Facilities:

- ❑ ADA
- ❑ Gift Shop
- ❑ Museum
- ❑ Visitor Center
- ❑ Restrooms

- ❑ Playground
- ❑ Picnic sites
- ❑
- ❑
- ❑

Memories of the Trip

Get the Facts

- ❑ Phone   (518) 268-2188
- ❑ Park Hours

  _____

- ❑ Reservations? _____ Y _____ N

  date made_____

- ❑ Open all year? _____ Y _____ N

  dates_____

- ❑ Dog friendly _____ Y _____ N

- ❑ Distance from home

  miles: _____

  hours: _____

- ❑ Address_____

  _____

  _____

Fees:

- ❑ Day Use $ _____
- ❑ Refund policy

  _____

  _____

  _____

Stamps & Stickers

Grafton Lakes State Park
City: Grafton   County: Rensselaer

Plan your trip: https://parks.ny.gov/parks/graftonlakes/details.aspx

Activities: (check all that apply)

- ❑ Beach
- ❑ Biking
- ❑ Boating
- ❑ Canoeing
- ❑ Fishing / Ice
- ❑ Hiking
- ❑ Horseback Riding
- ❑ Hunting
- ❑ Kayaking

- ❑ Marina
- ❑ Nature Center
- ❑ Photography
- ❑ Swimming
- ❑ Waterfalls
- ❑ Watersports
- ❑ Wildlife & Birding
- ❑ Winter Sports
- ❑

Facilities:

- ❑ ADA
- ❑ Gift Shop
- ❑ Museum
- ❑ Visitor Center
- ❑ Restrooms

- ❑ Playground
- ❑ Picnic sites
- ❑
- ❑
- ❑

Memories of the Trip

Get the Facts

- ❑ Phone   (518) 279-1155
- ❑ Park Hours

    _____

- ❑ Reservations? ____Y ____N

    date made_____

- ❑ Open all year? ____Y____N

    dates_____

- ❑ Dog friendly _____Y _____N
- ❑ Distance from home

    miles: _____

    hours: _____

- ❑ Address_____

    _____

    _____

Fees:

- ❑ Day Use $ _____
- ❑ Refund policy

    _____

    _____

    _____

Stamps & Stickers

Saratoga Spa State Park
City: Saratoga Springs   County: Saratoga

Plan your trip: https://parks.ny.gov/parks/saratogaspa/details.aspx

Activities: (check all that apply)

- ❑ Beach
- ❑ Biking
- ❑ Boating
- ❑ Canoeing
- ❑ Fishing / Ice
- ❑ Hiking
- ❑ Horseback Riding
- ❑ Hunting
- ❑ Kayaking

- ❑ Marina
- ❑ Nature Center
- ❑ Photography
- ❑ Swimming
- ❑ Waterfalls
- ❑ Watersports
- ❑ Wildlife & Birding
- ❑ Winter Sports
- ❑

Facilities:

- ❑ ADA
- ❑ Gift Shop
- ❑ Museum
- ❑ Visitor Center
- ❑ Restrooms

- ❑ Playground
- ❑ Picnic sites
- ❑
- ❑
- ❑

Memories of the Trip

Get the Facts

- ❑ Phone   (518) 584-2535
- ❑ Park Hours

  _____

- ❑ Reservations? ____Y ____N

  date made_____

- ❑ Open all year? ____Y____N

  dates_____

- ❑ Dog friendly _____Y _____N

- ❑ Distance from home

  miles: _____

  hours: _____

- ❑ Address_____

  _____

  _____

Fees:

- ❑ Day Use $ _____
- ❑ Refund policy

  _____

  _____

  _____

Stamps & Stickers

Mine Kill State Park
City: North Blenheim　　　County: Schoharie

Plan your trip: https://parks.ny.gov/parks/minekill/details.aspx

Activities: (check all that apply)

- ❑ Beach
- ❑ Biking
- ❑ Boating
- ❑ Canoeing
- ❑ Fishing / Ice
- ❑ Hiking
- ❑ Horseback Riding
- ❑ Hunting
- ❑ Kayaking

- ❑ Marina
- ❑ Nature Center
- ❑ Photography
- ❑ Swimming
- ❑ Waterfalls
- ❑ Watersports
- ❑ Wildlife & Birding
- ❑ Winter Sports
- ❑

Facilities:

- ❑ ADA
- ❑ Gift Shop
- ❑ Museum
- ❑ Visitor Center
- ❑ Restrooms

- ❑ Playground
- ❑ Picnic sites
- ❑
- ❑
- ❑

Memories of the Trip

Get the Facts

- ❑ Phone　(518) 827-6111
- ❑ Park Hours

_____

- ❑ Reservations? ____Y ____N

date made_____

- ❑ Open all year? ____Y____N

dates_____

- ❑ Dog friendly _____Y _____N
- ❑ Distance from home

miles: _____

hours: _____

- ❑ Address_____

_____

_____

Fees:

- ❑ Day Use $ _____
- ❑ Refund policy

_____

_____

_____

Stamps & Stickers

Notes:

Palisades Region

- Orange County
- Rockland County
- Sullivan County
- Ulster County

Bear Mountain State Park
City: Bear Mountain   County: Orange

Plan your trip: https://parks.ny.gov/parks/bearmountain/details.aspx

Activities:

- ❑ Biking
- ❑ Boating
- ❑ Canoeing
- ❑ Disc Golf
- ❑ Fishing / Ice
- ❑ Hiking
- ❑ Horseback Riding
- ❑ Hunting
- ❑ Kayaking
- ❑ Marina
- ❑ Nature Center / Trails
- ❑ Photography
- ❑ Playing Fields
- ❑ Scenic Views
- ❑ Swimming
- ❑ Waterfalls
- ❑ Wildlife & Birding
- ❑ Winter Sports
- ❑
- ❑
- ❑
- ❑

Facilities:

- ❑ ADA
- ❑ Picnic sites
- ❑ Restrooms
- ❑ Showers
- ❑ Trailer Access
- ❑ Visitor center
- ❑ Group Camping
- ❑ RV Camp
- ❑ Rustic Camping
- ❑ Cabins / Yurts
- ❑ Day Use Area
- ❑

Notes:

Get the Facts

- ❑ Phone   (845) 786-2701
- ❑ Park Hours

    _____

- ❑ Reservations? ____Y ____N

    date made_____

- ❑ Open all year ____Y_____N

    dates_____

- ❑ Check in time _____
- ❑ Check out time _____
- ❑ Pet friendly _____Y _____N
- ❑ Max RV length _____
- ❑ Distance from home

    miles: _____

    hours: _____

- ❑ Address_____

    _____

    _____

Fees:

- ❑ Day Use $ _____
- ❑ Camp Sites $ _____
- ❑ RV Sites $ _____
- ❑ Refund policy

    _____

    _____

    _____

Make It Personal

Trip dates:

The weather was: Sunny Cloudy Rainy Stormy Snowy Foggy Warm Cold

Why I went:

How I got there: (circle all that apply) Plane   Train   Car   Bus   Bike   Hike   RV   MC

I went with:

We stayed in (space, cabin # etc):

Most relaxing day:

Something funny:

Someone we met:

Best story told:

The kids liked this:

The best food:

Games played:

Something disappointing:

Next time I'll do this differently:

Lake Sebago Beach-Harriman State Park
City: Bear Mountain   County: Orange

Plan your trip: https://parks.ny.gov/parks/lakesebago/details.aspx

Activities:

- ❏ Biking
- ❏ Boating
- ❏ Canoeing
- ❏ Disc Golf
- ❏ Fishing / Ice
- ❏ Hiking
- ❏ Horseback Riding
- ❏ Hunting
- ❏ Kayaking
- ❏ Marina
- ❏ Nature Center / Trails

- ❏ Photography
- ❏ Playing Fields
- ❏ Scenic Views
- ❏ Swimming
- ❏ Waterfalls
- ❏ Wildlife & Birding
- ❏ Winter Sports
- ❏
- ❏
- ❏
- ❏

Facilities:

- ❏ ADA
- ❏ Picnic sites
- ❏ Restrooms
- ❏ Showers
- ❏ Trailer Access
- ❏ Visitor center

- ❏ Group Camping
- ❏ RV Camp
- ❏ Rustic Camping
- ❏ Cabins / Yurts
- ❏ Day Use Area
- ❏

Notes:

Get the Facts

- ❏ Phone   (845) 351-2583
- ❏ Park Hours

   _____

- ❏ Reservations? ____Y ____N

   date made_____

- ❏ Open all year ____Y ____N

   dates_____

- ❏ Check in time _____
- ❏ Check out time _____
- ❏ Pet friendly _____Y _____N
- ❏ Max RV length _____
- ❏ Distance from home

   miles: _____

   hours: _____

- ❏ Address_____

   _____

   _____

Fees:

- ❏ Day Use $ _____
- ❏ Camp Sites $ _____
- ❏ RV Sites $ _____
- ❏ Refund policy

   _____

   _____

   _____

Make It Personal

Trip dates: _____ | The weather was: Sunny Cloudy Rainy Stormy Snowy Foggy Warm Cold

Why I went:
_____

_____

How I got there: (circle all that apply)   Plane   Train   Car   Bus   Bike   Hike   RV   MC
_____

I went with:
_____

We stayed in (space, cabin # etc):
_____

Most relaxing day:
_____

_____

Something funny:
_____

_____

Someone we met:
_____

_____

Best story told:
_____

_____

The kids liked this:
_____

_____

The best food:
_____

_____

Games played:
_____

_____

Something disappointing:
_____

_____

Next time I'll do this differently:
_____

_____

Harriman State Park
City: Ramapo   County: Rockland

Plan your trip: https://parks.ny.gov/parks/harriman/details.aspx

Activities:

- ❑ Biking
- ❑ Boating
- ❑ Canoeing
- ❑ Disc Golf
- ❑ Fishing / Ice
- ❑ Hiking
- ❑ Horseback Riding
- ❑ Hunting
- ❑ Kayaking
- ❑ Marina
- ❑ Nature Center / Trails
- ❑ Photography
- ❑ Playing Fields
- ❑ Scenic Views
- ❑ Swimming
- ❑ Waterfalls
- ❑ Wildlife & Birding
- ❑ Winter Sports
- ❑
- ❑
- ❑
- ❑

Facilities:

- ❑ ADA
- ❑ Picnic sites
- ❑ Restrooms
- ❑ Showers
- ❑ Trailer Access
- ❑ Visitor center
- ❑ Group Camping
- ❑ RV Camp
- ❑ Rustic Camping
- ❑ Cabins / Yurts
- ❑ Day Use Area
- ❑

Notes:

Get the Facts

- ❑ Phone   (845) 947-2444
- ❑ Park Hours

_____

- ❑ Reservations? ____Y ____N

date made_____

- ❑ Open all year ____Y ____N

dates_____

- ❑ Check in time _____
- ❑ Check out time _____
- ❑ Pet friendly _____Y _____N
- ❑ Max RV length _____
- ❑ Distance from home

miles: _____

hours: _____

- ❑ Address_____

_____

_____

Fees:

- ❑ Day Use $ _____
- ❑ Camp Sites $ _____
- ❑ RV Sites $ _____
- ❑ Refund policy

_____

_____

_____

Make It Personal

Trip dates: _____ | The weather was: Sunny   Cloudy   Rainy   Stormy   Snowy   Foggy   Warm   Cold

Why I went:
_____

_____

How I got there: (circle all that apply)   Plane   Train   Car   Bus   Bike   Hike   RV   MC
_____

I went with:
_____

We stayed in (space, cabin # etc):
_____

Most relaxing day:
_____

_____

Something funny:
_____

_____

Someone we met:
_____

_____

Best story told:
_____

_____

The kids liked this:
_____

_____

The best food:
_____

_____

Games played:
_____

_____

Something disappointing:
_____

_____

Next time I'll do this differently:
_____

_____

Sebago Cabin Camp-Harriman State Park
City: Ramapo   County: Rockland

Plan your trip: https://parks.ny.gov/parks/campsebago/details.aspx

Activities:

- ❑ Biking
- ❑ Boating
- ❑ Canoeing
- ❑ Disc Golf
- ❑ Fishing / Ice
- ❑ Hiking
- ❑ Horseback Riding
- ❑ Hunting
- ❑ Kayaking
- ❑ Marina
- ❑ Nature Center / Trails
- ❑ Photography
- ❑ Playing Fields
- ❑ Scenic Views
- ❑ Swimming
- ❑ Waterfalls
- ❑ Wildlife & Birding
- ❑ Winter Sports
- ❑
- ❑
- ❑
- ❑

Facilities:

- ❑ ADA
- ❑ Picnic sites
- ❑ Restrooms
- ❑ Showers
- ❑ Trailer Access
- ❑ Visitor center
- ❑ Group Camping
- ❑ RV Camp
- ❑ Rustic Camping
- ❑ Cabins / Yurts
- ❑ Day Use Area
- ❑

Notes:

Get the Facts

- ❑ Phone   (845) 429-2039
- ❑ Park Hours

  _____

- ❑ Reservations? _____Y _____N

  date made_____

- ❑ Open all year _____Y_____N

  dates_____

- ❑ Check in time _____
- ❑ Check out time _____
- ❑ Pet friendly _____Y _____N
- ❑ Max RV length _____
- ❑ Distance from home

  miles: _____

  hours: _____

- ❑ Address_____

  _____

  _____

Fees:

- ❑ Day Use $ _____
- ❑ Camp Sites $ _____
- ❑ RV Sites $ _____
- ❑ Refund policy

  _____

  _____

  _____

Make It Personal

Trip dates:

The weather was: Sunny Cloudy Rainy Stormy Snowy Foggy Warm Cold

Why I went:

How I got there: (circle all that apply) Plane Train Car Bus Bike Hike RV MC

I went with:

We stayed in (space, cabin # etc):

Most relaxing day:

Something funny:

Someone we met:

Best story told:

The kids liked this:

The best food:

Games played:

Something disappointing:

Next time I'll do this differently:

Beaver Pond Campgrounds - Harriman State Park

City: Stony Point   County: Rockland

Plan your trip: https://parks.ny.gov/parks/beaverpond/details.aspx

Activities:

- ❑ Biking
- ❑ Boating
- ❑ Canoeing
- ❑ Disc Golf
- ❑ Fishing / Ice
- ❑ Hiking
- ❑ Horseback Riding
- ❑ Hunting
- ❑ Kayaking
- ❑ Marina
- ❑ Nature Center / Trails

- ❑ Photography
- ❑ Playing Fields
- ❑ Scenic Views
- ❑ Swimming
- ❑ Waterfalls
- ❑ Wildlife & Birding
- ❑ Winter Sports
- ❑
- ❑
- ❑
- ❑

Facilities:

- ❑ ADA
- ❑ Picnic sites
- ❑ Restrooms
- ❑ Showers
- ❑ Trailer Access
- ❑ Visitor center

- ❑ Group Camping
- ❑ RV Camp
- ❑ Rustic Camping
- ❑ Cabins / Yurts
- ❑ Day Use Area
- ❑

Notes:

Get the Facts

- ❑ Phone   (845) 947-2792
- ❑ Park Hours

  _____

- ❑ Reservations? ____Y ____N

  date made_____

- ❑ Open all year ____Y____N

  dates_____

- ❑ Check in time _____
- ❑ Check out time _____
- ❑ Pet friendly _____Y _____N
- ❑ Max RV length _____
- ❑ Distance from home

  miles: _____

  hours: _____

- ❑ Address_____

  _____

  _____

Fees:

- ❑ Day Use $ _____
- ❑ Camp Sites $ _____
- ❑ RV Sites $ _____
- ❑ Refund policy

  _____

  _____

  _____

Make It Personal

Trip dates: _____ | The weather was: Sunny Cloudy Rainy Stormy Snowy Foggy Warm Cold

Why I went: _____
_____

How I got there: (circle all that apply)   Plane   Train   Car   Bus   Bike   Hike   RV   MC
_____

I went with: _____

We stayed in (space, cabin # etc): _____

Most relaxing day: _____
_____

Something funny: _____
_____

Someone we met: _____
_____

Best story told: _____
_____

The kids liked this: _____
_____

The best food: _____
_____

Games played: _____
_____

Something disappointing: _____
_____

Next time I'll do this differently: _____
_____

Minnewaska State Park Preserve: Sam's Point Area

City: Cragsmoor   County: Ulster

Plan your trip: https://parks.ny.gov/parks/samspoint/details.aspx

Activities:

- ❑ Biking
- ❑ Boating
- ❑ Canoeing
- ❑ Disc Golf
- ❑ Fishing / Ice
- ❑ Hiking
- ❑ Horseback Riding
- ❑ Hunting
- ❑ Kayaking
- ❑ Marina
- ❑ Nature Center / Trails
- ❑ Photography
- ❑ Playing Fields
- ❑ Scenic Views
- ❑ Swimming
- ❑ Waterfalls
- ❑ Wildlife & Birding
- ❑ Winter Sports
- ❑
- ❑
- ❑
- ❑

Facilities:

- ❑ ADA
- ❑ Picnic sites
- ❑ Restrooms
- ❑ Showers
- ❑ Trailer Access
- ❑ Visitor center
- ❑ Group Camping
- ❑ RV Camp
- ❑ Rustic Camping
- ❑ Cabins / Yurts
- ❑ Day Use Area
- ❑

Notes:

Get the Facts

- ❑ Phone   (845) 647-7989
- ❑ Park Hours

  _____

- ❑ Reservations? _____Y _____N

  date made_____

- ❑ Open all year _____Y_____N

  dates_____

- ❑ Check in time _____
- ❑ Check out time _____
- ❑ Pet friendly _____Y _____N
- ❑ Max RV length _____
- ❑ Distance from home

  miles: _____

  hours: _____

- ❑ Address_____

  _____

  _____

Fees:

- ❑ Day Use $ _____
- ❑ Camp Sites $ _____
- ❑ RV Sites $ _____
- ❑ Refund policy

  _____

  _____

  _____

Make It Personal

Trip dates:
_____

The weather was: Sunny Cloudy Rainy Stormy Snowy Foggy Warm Cold

Why I went:
_____

_____

How I got there: (circle all that apply)   Plane   Train   Car   Bus   Bike   Hike   RV   MC
_____

I went with:
_____

We stayed in (space, cabin # etc):
_____

Most relaxing day:
_____

_____

Something funny:
_____

_____

Someone we met:
_____

_____

Best story told:
_____

_____

The kids liked this:
_____

_____

The best food:
_____

_____

Games played:
_____

_____

Something disappointing:
_____

_____

Next time I'll do this differently:
_____

_____

Minnewaska State Park Preserve
City: Kerhonkson   County: Ulster

Plan your trip: https://parks.ny.gov/parks/minnewaska/details.aspx

Activities:

- ❑ Biking
- ❑ Boating
- ❑ Canoeing
- ❑ Disc Golf
- ❑ Fishing / Ice
- ❑ Hiking
- ❑ Horseback Riding
- ❑ Hunting
- ❑ Kayaking
- ❑ Marina
- ❑ Nature Center / Trails

- ❑ Photography
- ❑ Playing Fields
- ❑ Scenic Views
- ❑ Swimming
- ❑ Waterfalls
- ❑ Wildlife & Birding
- ❑ Winter Sports
- ❑
- ❑
- ❑
- ❑

Facilities:

- ❑ ADA
- ❑ Picnic sites
- ❑ Restrooms
- ❑ Showers
- ❑ Trailer Access
- ❑ Visitor center

- ❑ Group Camping
- ❑ RV Camp
- ❑ Rustic Camping
- ❑ Cabins / Yurts
- ❑ Day Use Area
- ❑

Notes:

Get the Facts

- ❑ Phone   (845) 255-0752
- ❑ Park Hours

_____

- ❑ Reservations? _____Y _____N

date made_____

- ❑ Open all year _____Y_____N

dates_____

- ❑ Check in time _____
- ❑ Check out time _____
- ❑ Pet friendly _____Y _____N
- ❑ Max RV length _____
- ❑ Distance from home

miles: _____

hours: _____

- ❑ Address_____

_____

_____

Fees:

- ❑ Day Use $ _____
- ❑ Camp Sites $ _____
- ❑ RV Sites $ _____
- ❑ Refund policy

_____

_____

_____

Make It Personal

Trip dates: _____ | The weather was: Sunny Cloudy Rainy Stormy Snowy Foggy Warm Cold

Why I went: _____

_____

How I got there: (circle all that apply) Plane Train Car Bus Bike Hike RV MC

I went with: _____

We stayed in (space, cabin # etc): _____

Most relaxing day: _____

_____

Something funny: _____

_____

Someone we met: _____

_____

Best story told: _____

_____

The kids liked this: _____

_____

The best food: _____

_____

Games played: _____

_____

Something disappointing: _____

_____

Next time I'll do this differently: _____

_____

Anthony Wayne Recreation Area-Harriman State Park

City: Bear Mountain   County: Orange

Plan your trip: https://parks.ny.gov/parks/anthonywayne/details.aspx

Activities: (check all that apply)

- ❑ Beach
- ❑ Biking
- ❑ Boating
- ❑ Canoeing
- ❑ Fishing / Ice
- ❑ Hiking
- ❑ Horseback Riding
- ❑ Hunting
- ❑ Kayaking

- ❑ Marina
- ❑ Nature Center
- ❑ Photography
- ❑ Swimming
- ❑ Waterfalls
- ❑ Watersports
- ❑ Wildlife & Birding
- ❑ Winter Sports
- ❑

Facilities:

- ❑ ADA
- ❑ Gift Shop
- ❑ Museum
- ❑ Visitor Center
- ❑ Restrooms

- ❑ Playground
- ❑ Picnic sites
- ❑
- ❑
- ❑

Memories of the Trip

Get the Facts

- ❑ Phone   (845) 942-2560
- ❑ Park Hours

  _____

- ❑ Reservations? ____Y ____N

  date made_____

- ❑ Open all year? ____Y____N

  dates_____

- ❑ Dog friendly _____Y _____N

- ❑ Distance from home

  miles: _____

  hours: _____

- ❑ Address_____

  _____

  _____

Fees:

- ❑ Day Use $ _____
- ❑ Refund policy

  _____

  _____

  _____

Stamps & Stickers

Silver Mine - Harriman State Park
City: Bear Mountain   County: Orange

Plan your trip: https://parks.ny.gov/parks/silvermine/details.aspx

Activities: (check all that apply)

- ❑ Beach
- ❑ Biking
- ❑ Boating
- ❑ Canoeing
- ❑ Fishing / Ice
- ❑ Hiking
- ❑ Horseback Riding
- ❑ Hunting
- ❑ Kayaking

- ❑ Marina
- ❑ Nature Center
- ❑ Photography
- ❑ Swimming
- ❑ Waterfalls
- ❑ Watersports
- ❑ Wildlife & Birding
- ❑ Winter Sports
- ❑

Facilities:

- ❑ ADA
- ❑ Gift Shop
- ❑ Museum
- ❑ Visitor Center
- ❑ Restrooms

- ❑ Playground
- ❑ Picnic sites
- ❑
- ❑
- ❑

Memories of the Trip

Get the Facts

- ❑ Phone   (845) 429-8257
- ❑ Park Hours

  _____

- ❑ Reservations? _____Y _____N

  date made_____

- ❑ Open all year? _____Y_____N

  dates_____

- ❑ Dog friendly _____Y _____N

- ❑ Distance from home

  miles: _____

  hours: _____

- ❑ Address_____

  _____

  _____

Fees:

- ❑ Day Use $ _____
- ❑ Refund policy

  _____

  _____

  _____

Stamps & Stickers

Goosepond Mountain State Park

City: Chester　　　　　　　**County: Orange**

Plan your trip: https://parks.ny.gov/parks/goosepondmountain/details.aspx

Activities: (check all that apply)

- ❑ Beach
- ❑ Biking
- ❑ Boating
- ❑ Canoeing
- ❑ Fishing / Ice
- ❑ Hiking
- ❑ Horseback Riding
- ❑ Hunting
- ❑ Kayaking

- ❑ Marina
- ❑ Nature Center
- ❑ Photography
- ❑ Swimming
- ❑ Waterfalls
- ❑ Watersports
- ❑ Wildlife & Birding
- ❑ Winter Sports
- ❑

Facilities:

- ❑ ADA
- ❑ Gift Shop
- ❑ Museum
- ❑ Visitor Center
- ❑ Restrooms

- ❑ Playground
- ❑ Picnic sites
- ❑
- ❑
- ❑

Memories of the Trip

Get the Facts

- ❑ Phone　(845) 786-2701
- ❑ Park Hours

　_____

- ❑ Reservations? ____Y ____N

　date made_____

- ❑ Open all year? ____Y____N

　dates_____

- ❑ Dog friendly _____Y _____N
- ❑ Distance from home

　miles: _____

　hours: _____

- ❑ Address_____

　_____

　_____

Fees:

- ❑ Day Use $ _____
- ❑ Refund policy

　_____

　_____

　_____

Stamps & Stickers

Storm King State Park
City: Cornwall-on-Hudson   County: Orange

Plan your trip: https://parks.ny.gov/parks/stormking/details.aspx

Activities: (check all that apply)

- ❑ Beach
- ❑ Biking
- ❑ Boating
- ❑ Canoeing
- ❑ Fishing / Ice
- ❑ Hiking
- ❑ Horseback Riding
- ❑ Hunting
- ❑ Kayaking

- ❑ Marina
- ❑ Nature Center
- ❑ Photography
- ❑ Swimming
- ❑ Waterfalls
- ❑ Watersports
- ❑ Wildlife & Birding
- ❑ Winter Sports
- ❑

Facilities:

- ❑ ADA
- ❑ Gift Shop
- ❑ Museum
- ❑ Visitor Center
- ❑ Restrooms

- ❑ Playground
- ❑ Picnic sites
- ❑
- ❑
- ❑

Memories of the Trip

Get the Facts

- ❑ Phone   (845) 786-2701
- ❑ Park Hours

  _____

- ❑ Reservations? _____Y _____N

  date made_____

- ❑ Open all year? _____Y_____N

  dates_____

- ❑ Dog friendly _____Y _____N

- ❑ Distance from home

  miles: _____

  hours: _____

- ❑ Address_____

  _____

  _____

Fees:

- ❑ Day Use $ _____
- ❑ Refund policy

  _____

  _____

  _____

Stamps & Stickers

Highland Lakes State Park
City: Middletown   County: Orange

Plan your trip: https://parks.ny.gov/parks/highlandlakes/details.aspx

Activities: (check all that apply)

- ❑ Beach
- ❑ Biking
- ❑ Boating
- ❑ Canoeing
- ❑ Fishing / Ice
- ❑ Hiking
- ❑ Horseback Riding
- ❑ Hunting
- ❑ Kayaking

- ❑ Marina
- ❑ Nature Center
- ❑ Photography
- ❑ Swimming
- ❑ Waterfalls
- ❑ Watersports
- ❑ Wildlife & Birding
- ❑ Winter Sports
- ❑

Facilities:

- ❑ ADA
- ❑ Gift Shop
- ❑ Museum
- ❑ Visitor Center
- ❑ Restrooms

- ❑ Playground
- ❑ Picnic sites
- ❑
- ❑
- ❑

Memories of the Trip

Get the Facts

- ❑ Phone   (845) 786-2701
- ❑ Park Hours

  _____

- ❑ Reservations? _____Y _____N

  date made_____

- ❑ Open all year? _____Y_____N

  dates_____

- ❑ Dog friendly _____Y _____N
- ❑ Distance from home

  miles: _____

  hours: _____

- ❑ Address_____

  _____

  _____

Fees:

- ❑ Day Use $ _____
- ❑ Refund policy

  _____

  _____

  _____

Stamps & Stickers

Schunnemunk State Park

City: New Windsor   County: Orange

Plan your trip: https://parks.ny.gov/parks/schunnemunk/details.aspx

Activities: (check all that apply)

- ❑ Beach
- ❑ Biking
- ❑ Boating
- ❑ Canoeing
- ❑ Fishing / Ice
- ❑ Hiking
- ❑ Horseback Riding
- ❑ Hunting
- ❑ Kayaking

- ❑ Marina
- ❑ Nature Center
- ❑ Photography
- ❑ Swimming
- ❑ Waterfalls
- ❑ Watersports
- ❑ Wildlife & Birding
- ❑ Winter Sports
- ❑

Facilities:

- ❑ ADA
- ❑ Gift Shop
- ❑ Museum
- ❑ Visitor Center
- ❑ Restrooms

- ❑ Playground
- ❑ Picnic sites
- ❑
- ❑
- ❑

Memories of the Trip

Get the Facts

- ❑ Phone   (845) 351-5907
- ❑ Park Hours

  _____

- ❑ Reservations? _____Y _____N

  date made_____

- ❑ Open all year? _____Y _____N

  dates_____

- ❑ Dog friendly _____Y _____N

- ❑ Distance from home

  miles: _____

  hours: _____

- ❑ Address_____

  _____

  _____

Fees:

- ❑ Day Use $ _____
- ❑ Refund policy

  _____

  _____

  _____

Stamps & Stickers

Lake Tiorati Beach-Harriman State Park
City: Southfields   County: Orange

Plan your trip: https://parks.ny.gov/parks/laketiorati/details.aspx

Activities: (check all that apply)

- ❏ Beach
- ❏ Biking
- ❏ Boating
- ❏ Canoeing
- ❏ Fishing / Ice
- ❏ Hiking
- ❏ Horseback Riding
- ❏ Hunting
- ❏ Kayaking

- ❏ Marina
- ❏ Nature Center
- ❏ Photography
- ❏ Swimming
- ❏ Waterfalls
- ❏ Watersports
- ❏ Wildlife & Birding
- ❏ Winter Sports
- ❏

Facilities:

- ❏ ADA
- ❏ Gift Shop
- ❏ Museum
- ❏ Visitor Center
- ❏ Restrooms

- ❏ Playground
- ❏ Picnic sites
- ❏
- ❏
- ❏

Memories of the Trip

Get the Facts

- ❏ Phone   (845) 429-8257
- ❏ Park Hours

  _____

- ❏ Reservations? ____Y ____N

  date made_____

- ❏ Open all year? ____Y____N

  dates_____

- ❏ Dog friendly _____Y _____N

- ❏ Distance from home

  miles: _____

  hours: _____

- ❏ Address_____

  _____

  _____

Fees:

- ❏ Day Use $ _____
- ❏ Refund policy

  _____

  _____

  _____

Stamps & Stickers

Sterling Forest State Park
City: Tuxedo   County: Orange

Plan your trip: https://parks.ny.gov/parks/sterlingforest/details.aspx

Activities: (check all that apply)

- ❑ Beach
- ❑ Biking
- ❑ Boating
- ❑ Canoeing
- ❑ Fishing / Ice
- ❑ Hiking
- ❑ Horseback Riding
- ❑ Hunting
- ❑ Kayaking

- ❑ Marina
- ❑ Nature Center
- ❑ Photography
- ❑ Swimming
- ❑ Waterfalls
- ❑ Watersports
- ❑ Wildlife & Birding
- ❑ Winter Sports
- ❑

Facilities:

- ❑ ADA
- ❑ Gift Shop
- ❑ Museum
- ❑ Visitor Center
- ❑ Restrooms

- ❑ Playground
- ❑ Picnic sites
- ❑
- ❑
- ❑

Memories of the Trip

Get the Facts

- ❑ Phone   (845) 351-5907
- ❑ Park Hours

  _____

- ❑ Reservations? ____Y ____N

  date made_____

- ❑ Open all year? ____Y____N

  dates_____

- ❑ Dog friendly _____Y _____N

- ❑ Distance from home

  miles: _____

  hours: _____

- ❑ Address_____

  _____

  _____

Fees:

- ❑ Day Use $ _____
- ❑ Refund policy

  _____

  _____

  _____

Stamps & Stickers

Blauvelt State Park

City: Blauvelt   County: Rockland

Plan your trip: https://parks.ny.gov/parks/blauvelt/details.aspx

Activities: (check all that apply)

- ❏ Beach
- ❏ Biking
- ❏ Boating
- ❏ Canoeing
- ❏ Fishing / Ice
- ❏ Hiking
- ❏ Horseback Riding
- ❏ Hunting
- ❏ Kayaking

- ❏ Marina
- ❏ Nature Center
- ❏ Photography
- ❏ Swimming
- ❏ Waterfalls
- ❏ Watersports
- ❏ Wildlife & Birding
- ❏ Winter Sports
- ❏

Facilities:

- ❏ ADA
- ❏ Gift Shop
- ❏ Museum
- ❏ Visitor Center
- ❏ Restrooms

- ❏ Playground
- ❏ Picnic sites
- ❏
- ❏
- ❏

Memories of the Trip

Get the Facts

- ❏ Phone   (845) 359-0544
- ❏ Park Hours

  _____

- ❏ Reservations? _____ Y _____ N

  date made_____

- ❏ Open all year? _____ Y _____ N

  dates_____

- ❏ Dog friendly _____ Y _____ N

- ❏ Distance from home

  miles: _____

  hours: _____

- ❏ Address_____

  _____

  _____

Fees:

- ❏ Day Use $ _____
- ❏ Refund policy

  _____

  _____

  _____

Stamps & Stickers

High Tor State Park
City: New City   County: Rockland

Plan your trip: https://parks.ny.gov/parks/hightor/details.aspx

Activities: (check all that apply)

- ❑ Beach
- ❑ Biking
- ❑ Boating
- ❑ Canoeing
- ❑ Fishing / Ice
- ❑ Hiking
- ❑ Horseback Riding
- ❑ Hunting
- ❑ Kayaking

- ❑ Marina
- ❑ Nature Center
- ❑ Photography
- ❑ Swimming
- ❑ Waterfalls
- ❑ Watersports
- ❑ Wildlife & Birding
- ❑ Winter Sports
- ❑

Facilities:

- ❑ ADA
- ❑ Gift Shop
- ❑ Museum
- ❑ Visitor Center
- ❑ Restrooms

- ❑ Playground
- ❑ Picnic sites
- ❑
- ❑
- ❑

Memories of the Trip

Get the Facts

- ❑ Phone   (845) 634-8074
- ❑ Park Hours

  _____

- ❑ Reservations? ____Y ____N

  date made_____

- ❑ Open all year? ____Y____N

  dates_____

- ❑ Dog friendly _____Y _____N

- ❑ Distance from home

  miles: _____

  hours: _____

- ❑ Address_____

  _____

  _____

Fees:

- ❑ Day Use $ _____
- ❑ Refund policy

  _____

  _____

  _____

Stamps & Stickers

Tallman Mountain State Park

City: Sparkill   County: Rockland

Plan your trip: https://parks.ny.gov/parks/tallman/details.aspx

Activities: (check all that apply)

- ❏ Beach
- ❏ Biking
- ❏ Boating
- ❏ Canoeing
- ❏ Fishing / Ice
- ❏ Hiking
- ❏ Horseback Riding
- ❏ Hunting
- ❏ Kayaking

- ❏ Marina
- ❏ Nature Center
- ❏ Photography
- ❏ Swimming
- ❏ Waterfalls
- ❏ Watersports
- ❏ Wildlife & Birding
- ❏ Winter Sports
- ❏

Facilities:

- ❏ ADA
- ❏ Gift Shop
- ❏ Museum
- ❏ Visitor Center
- ❏ Restrooms

- ❏ Playground
- ❏ Picnic sites
- ❏
- ❏
- ❏

Memories of the Trip

Get the Facts

- ❏ Phone   (845) 359-0544
- ❏ Park Hours

  _____

- ❏ Reservations? ____Y ____N

  date made_____

- ❏ Open all year? ____Y____N

  dates_____

- ❏ Dog friendly _____Y _____N

- ❏ Distance from home

  miles: _____

  hours: _____

- ❏ Address_____

  _____

  _____

Fees:

- ❏ Day Use $ _____
- ❏ Refund policy

  _____

  _____

  _____

Stamps & Stickers

Lake Welch Beach-Harriman State Park

City: Stony Point   **County: Rockland**

Plan your trip: https://parks.ny.gov/parks/lakewelch/details.aspx

Activities: (check all that apply)

- ❏ Beach
- ❏ Biking
- ❏ Boating
- ❏ Canoeing
- ❏ Fishing / Ice
- ❏ Hiking
- ❏ Horseback Riding
- ❏ Hunting
- ❏ Kayaking
- ❏ Marina
- ❏ Nature Center
- ❏ Photography
- ❏ Swimming
- ❏ Waterfalls
- ❏ Watersports
- ❏ Wildlife & Birding
- ❏ Winter Sports
- ❏

Facilities:

- ❏ ADA
- ❏ Gift Shop
- ❏ Museum
- ❏ Visitor Center
- ❏ Restrooms
- ❏ Playground
- ❏ Picnic sites
- ❏
- ❏
- ❏

Memories of the Trip

Get the Facts

- ❏ Phone   (845) 947-2444
- ❏ Park Hours

  _____

- ❏ Reservations? ____Y ____N

  date made_____

- ❏ Open all year? ____Y____N

  dates_____

- ❏ Dog friendly ____Y ____N

- ❏ Distance from home

  miles: _____

  hours: _____

- ❏ Address_____

  _____

  _____

Fees:

- ❏ Day Use $ _____
- ❏ Refund policy

  _____
  _____
  _____

Stamps & Stickers

Nyack Beach State Park
City: Upper Nyack   County: Rockland

Plan your trip: https://parks.ny.gov/parks/nyackbeach/details.aspx

Activities: (check all that apply)

- ❑ Beach
- ❑ Biking
- ❑ Boating
- ❑ Canoeing
- ❑ Fishing / Ice
- ❑ Hiking
- ❑ Horseback Riding
- ❑ Hunting
- ❑ Kayaking

- ❑ Marina
- ❑ Nature Center
- ❑ Photography
- ❑ Swimming
- ❑ Waterfalls
- ❑ Watersports
- ❑ Wildlife & Birding
- ❑ Winter Sports
- ❑

Facilities:

- ❑ ADA
- ❑ Gift Shop
- ❑ Museum
- ❑ Visitor Center
- ❑ Restrooms

- ❑ Playground
- ❑ Picnic sites
- ❑
- ❑
- ❑

Memories of the Trip

Get the Facts

- ❑ Phone   (845) 268-3020
- ❑ Park Hours

_____

- ❑ Reservations? _____Y _____N

date made_____

- ❑ Open all year? _____Y_____N

dates_____

- ❑ Dog friendly _____Y _____N
- ❑ Distance from home

miles: _____

hours: _____

- ❑ Address_____

_____

_____

Fees:

- ❑ Day Use $ _____
- ❑ Refund policy

_____

_____

_____

Stamps & Stickers

Rockland Lake State Park

City: Valley Cottage   County: Rockland

Plan your trip: https://parks.ny.gov/parks/rocklandlake/details.aspx

Activities: (check all that apply)

- ❑ Beach
- ❑ Biking
- ❑ Boating
- ❑ Canoeing
- ❑ Fishing / Ice
- ❑ Hiking
- ❑ Horseback Riding
- ❑ Hunting
- ❑ Kayaking

- ❑ Marina
- ❑ Nature Center
- ❑ Photography
- ❑ Swimming
- ❑ Waterfalls
- ❑ Watersports
- ❑ Wildlife & Birding
- ❑ Winter Sports
- ❑

Facilities:

- ❑ ADA
- ❑ Gift Shop
- ❑ Museum
- ❑ Visitor Center
- ❑ Restrooms

- ❑ Playground
- ❑ Picnic sites
- ❑
- ❑
- ❑

Memories of the Trip

Get the Facts

- ❑ Phone   (845) 268-3020
- ❑ Park Hours

  _____

- ❑ Reservations? ____Y ____N

  date made_____

- ❑ Open all year? ____Y____N

  dates_____

- ❑ Dog friendly _____Y _____N
- ❑ Distance from home

  miles: _____

  hours: _____

- ❑ Address_____

  _____

  _____

Fees:

- ❑ Day Use $ _____
- ❑ Refund policy

  _____

  _____

  _____

Stamps & Stickers

Lake Superior State Park

City: Bethel   **County: Sullivan**

Plan your trip: https://parks.ny.gov/parks/lakesuperior/details.aspx

Activities: (check all that apply)

- ❏ Beach
- ❏ Biking
- ❏ Boating
- ❏ Canoeing
- ❏ Fishing / Ice
- ❏ Hiking
- ❏ Horseback Riding
- ❏ Hunting
- ❏ Kayaking

- ❏ Marina
- ❏ Nature Center
- ❏ Photography
- ❏ Swimming
- ❏ Waterfalls
- ❏ Watersports
- ❏ Wildlife & Birding
- ❏ Winter Sports
- ❏

Facilities:

- ❏ ADA
- ❏ Gift Shop
- ❏ Museum
- ❏ Visitor Center
- ❏ Restrooms

- ❏ Playground
- ❏ Picnic sites
- ❏
- ❏
- ❏

Memories of the Trip

| |
| |
| |
| |
| |
| |
| |
| |
| |
| |
| |
| |
| |
| |
| |
| |

Get the Facts

- ❏ Phone   (845) 807-0287
- ❏ Park Hours

  _____

- ❏ Reservations? ____Y ____N

  date made_____

- ❏ Open all year? ____Y____N

  dates_____

- ❏ Dog friendly _____Y _____N

- ❏ Distance from home

  miles: _____

  hours: _____

- ❏ Address_____

  _____

  _____

Fees:

- ❏ Day Use $ _____
- ❏ Refund policy

  _____

  _____

  _____

Stamps & Stickers

Franny Reese State Park
City: Highland   County: Ulster

Plan your trip: https://parks.ny.gov/parks/frannyreese/details.aspx

Activities: (check all that apply)

- ❑ Beach
- ❑ Biking
- ❑ Boating
- ❑ Canoeing
- ❑ Fishing / Ice
- ❑ Hiking
- ❑ Horseback Riding
- ❑ Hunting
- ❑ Kayaking

- ❑ Marina
- ❑ Nature Center
- ❑ Photography
- ❑ Swimming
- ❑ Waterfalls
- ❑ Watersports
- ❑ Wildlife & Birding
- ❑ Winter Sports
- ❑

Facilities:

- ❑ ADA
- ❑ Gift Shop
- ❑ Museum
- ❑ Visitor Center
- ❑ Restrooms

- ❑ Playground
- ❑ Picnic sites
- ❑
- ❑
- ❑

Memories of the Trip

Get the Facts

- ❑ Phone   (845) 473-4440
- ❑ Park Hours

  _____

- ❑ Reservations? ____Y ____N

  date made_____

- ❑ Open all year? ____Y____N

  dates_____

- ❑ Dog friendly _____Y _____N
- ❑ Distance from home

  miles: _____

  hours: _____

- ❑ Address_____

  _____

  _____

Fees:

- ❑ Day Use $ _____
- ❑ Refund policy

  _____

  _____

  _____

Stamps & Stickers

National Wildlife Refuges in New York

There are 10 National Wildlife Refuges in New York. Why not add these to your bucket list?

- ❑ Amangansett National Wildlife Refuge
- ❑ Conscience Point National Wildlife Refuge
- ❑ Elizabeth A Morton National Wildlife Refuge
- ❑ Iroquois National Wildlife Refuge
- ❑ Montezuma National Wildlife Refuge
- ❑ Oyster Bay National Wildlife Refuge
- ❑ Seatuck National Wildlife Refuge
- ❑ Shawangunk Grasslands National Wildlife Refuge
- ❑ Target Rock River National Wildlife Refuge
- ❑ Wertheim National Wildlife Refuge

Taconic Region

- Columbia County
- Dutchess County
- Putnam County
- Westchester County

Lake Taghkanic State Park
City: Ancram   County: Columbia

Plan your trip: https://parks.ny.gov/parks/laketaghkanic/details.aspx

Activities:

- ❑ Biking
- ❑ Boating
- ❑ Canoeing
- ❑ Disc Golf
- ❑ Fishing / Ice
- ❑ Hiking
- ❑ Horseback Riding
- ❑ Hunting
- ❑ Kayaking
- ❑ Marina
- ❑ Nature Center / Trails

- ❑ Photography
- ❑ Playing Fields
- ❑ Scenic Views
- ❑ Swimming
- ❑ Waterfalls
- ❑ Wildlife & Birding
- ❑ Winter Sports
- ❑
- ❑
- ❑
- ❑

Facilities:

- ❑ ADA
- ❑ Picnic sites
- ❑ Restrooms
- ❑ Showers
- ❑ Trailer Access
- ❑ Visitor center

- ❑ Group Camping
- ❑ RV Camp
- ❑ Rustic Camping
- ❑ Cabins / Yurts
- ❑ Day Use Area
- ❑

Notes:

Get the Facts

- ❑ Phone   (518) 851-3631
- ❑ Park Hours

_____

- ❑ Reservations? _____ Y _____ N

date made_____

- ❑ Open all year _____ Y _____ N

dates_____

- ❑ Check in time _____
- ❑ Check out time _____
- ❑ Pet friendly _____ Y _____ N
- ❑ Max RV length _____
- ❑ Distance from home

miles: _____

hours: _____

- ❑ Address_____

_____

_____

Fees:

- ❑ Day Use $ _____
- ❑ Camp Sites $ _____
- ❑ RV Sites $ _____
- ❑ Refund policy

_____

_____

_____

Make It Personal

Trip dates: _____

The weather was: Sunny Cloudy Rainy Stormy Snowy Foggy Warm Cold

Why I went:
_____
_____

How I got there: (circle all that apply) Plane Train Car Bus Bike Hike RV MC

I went with:
_____

We stayed in (space, cabin # etc):
_____

Most relaxing day:
_____
_____

Something funny:
_____
_____

Someone we met:
_____
_____

Best story told:
_____
_____

The kids liked this:
_____
_____

The best food:
_____
_____

Games played:
_____
_____

Something disappointing:
_____
_____

Next time I'll do this differently:
_____
_____

Taconic State Park-Copake Falls Area
City: Copake Falls   County: Columbia

Plan your trip: https://parks.ny.gov/parks/taconiccopake/details.aspx

Activities:

- ❑ Biking
- ❑ Boating
- ❑ Canoeing
- ❑ Disc Golf
- ❑ Fishing / Ice
- ❑ Hiking
- ❑ Horseback Riding
- ❑ Hunting
- ❑ Kayaking
- ❑ Marina
- ❑ Nature Center / Trails

- ❑ Photography
- ❑ Playing Fields
- ❑ Scenic Views
- ❑ Swimming
- ❑ Waterfalls
- ❑ Wildlife & Birding
- ❑ Winter Sports
- ❑
- ❑
- ❑
- ❑

Facilities:

- ❑ ADA
- ❑ Picnic sites
- ❑ Restrooms
- ❑ Showers
- ❑ Trailer Access
- ❑ Visitor center

- ❑ Group Camping
- ❑ RV Camp
- ❑ Rustic Camping
- ❑ Cabins / Yurts
- ❑ Day Use Area
- ❑

Notes:

Get the Facts

- ❑ Phone   (518) 329-3993
- ❑ Park Hours

  _____

- ❑ Reservations? ____Y ____N

  date made_____

- ❑ Open all year ____Y____N

  dates_____

- ❑ Check in time _____
- ❑ Check out time _____
- ❑ Pet friendly _____Y _____N
- ❑ Max RV length _____
- ❑ Distance from home

  miles: _____

  hours: _____

- ❑ Address_____

  _____

  _____

Fees:

- ❑ Day Use $ _____
- ❑ Camp Sites $ _____
- ❑ RV Sites $ _____
- ❑ Refund policy

  _____

  _____

  _____

Make It Personal

Trip dates: _____ | The weather was: Sunny Cloudy Rainy Stormy Snowy Foggy Warm Cold

_____

Why I went:
_____
_____

How I got there: (circle all that apply)   Plane   Train   Car   Bus   Bike   Hike   RV   MC
_____

I went with:
_____

We stayed in (space, cabin # etc):
_____

Most relaxing day:
_____
_____

Something funny:
_____
_____

Someone we met:
_____
_____

Best story told:
_____
_____

The kids liked this:
_____
_____

The best food:
_____
_____

Games played:
_____
_____

Something disappointing:
_____
_____

Next time I'll do this differently:
_____
_____

Taconic State Park-Rudd Pond Area
City: Millerton   County: Dutchess

Plan your trip: https://parks.ny.gov/parks/taconicruddpond/details.aspx

Activities:

- ❑ Biking
- ❑ Boating
- ❑ Canoeing
- ❑ Disc Golf
- ❑ Fishing / Ice
- ❑ Hiking
- ❑ Horseback Riding
- ❑ Hunting
- ❑ Kayaking
- ❑ Marina
- ❑ Nature Center / Trails

- ❑ Photography
- ❑ Playing Fields
- ❑ Scenic Views
- ❑ Swimming
- ❑ Waterfalls
- ❑ Wildlife & Birding
- ❑ Winter Sports
- ❑
- ❑
- ❑
- ❑

Facilities:

- ❑ ADA
- ❑ Picnic sites
- ❑ Restrooms
- ❑ Showers
- ❑ Trailer Access
- ❑ Visitor center

- ❑ Group Camping
- ❑ RV Camp
- ❑ Rustic Camping
- ❑ Cabins / Yurts
- ❑ Day Use Area
- ❑

Notes:

Get the Facts

- ❑ Phone   (518) 789-3059
- ❑ Park Hours

_____

- ❑ Reservations? _____Y _____N

date made_____

- ❑ Open all year _____Y_____N

dates_____

- ❑ Check in time _____
- ❑ Check out time _____
- ❑ Pet friendly _____Y _____N
- ❑ Max RV length _____
- ❑ Distance from home

miles: _____

hours: _____

- ❑ Address_____

_____

_____

Fees:

- ❑ Day Use $ _____
- ❑ Camp Sites $ _____
- ❑ RV Sites $ _____
- ❑ Refund policy

_____

_____

_____

Make It Personal

Trip dates: _____ | The weather was: Sunny Cloudy Rainy Stormy Snowy Foggy Warm Cold

Why I went:
_____

_____

How I got there: (circle all that apply)   Plane   Train   Car   Bus   Bike   Hike   RV   MC
_____

I went with:
_____

We stayed in (space, cabin # etc):
_____

Most relaxing day:
_____

_____

Something funny:
_____

_____

Someone we met:
_____

_____

Best story told:
_____

_____

The kids liked this:
_____

_____

The best food:
_____

_____

Games played:
_____

_____

Something disappointing:
_____

_____

Next time I'll do this differently:
_____

_____

Mills Norrie State Park
City: Staatsburg   County: Dutchess

Plan your trip: https://parks.ny.gov/parks/millsnorrie/details.aspx

Activities:

- ❏ Biking
- ❏ Boating
- ❏ Canoeing
- ❏ Disc Golf
- ❏ Fishing / Ice
- ❏ Hiking
- ❏ Horseback Riding
- ❏ Hunting
- ❏ Kayaking
- ❏ Marina
- ❏ Nature Center / Trails

- ❏ Photography
- ❏ Playing Fields
- ❏ Scenic Views
- ❏ Swimming
- ❏ Waterfalls
- ❏ Wildlife & Birding
- ❏ Winter Sports
- ❏
- ❏
- ❏
- ❏

Facilities:

- ❏ ADA
- ❏ Picnic sites
- ❏ Restrooms
- ❏ Showers
- ❏ Trailer Access
- ❏ Visitor center

- ❏ Group Camping
- ❏ RV Camp
- ❏ Rustic Camping
- ❏ Cabins / Yurts
- ❏ Day Use Area
- ❏

Notes:

Get the Facts

- ❏ Phone   (845) 889-4646
- ❏ Park Hours

  _____

- ❏ Reservations? ____Y ____N

  date made_____

- ❏ Open all year ____Y____N

  dates_____

- ❏ Check in time _____
- ❏ Check out time _____
- ❏ Pet friendly _____Y _____N
- ❏ Max RV length _____
- ❏ Distance from home

  miles: _____

  hours: _____

- ❏ Address_____

  _____

  _____

Fees:

- ❏ Day Use $ _____
- ❏ Camp Sites $ _____
- ❏ RV Sites $ _____
- ❏ Refund policy

  _____

  _____

  _____

Make It Personal

Trip dates: _____ | The weather was: Sunny Cloudy Rainy Stormy Snowy Foggy Warm Cold

Why I went:
_____
_____

How I got there: (circle all that apply) Plane Train Car Bus Bike Hike RV MC
_____

I went with:
_____

We stayed in (space, cabin # etc):
_____

Most relaxing day:
_____
_____

Something funny:
_____
_____

Someone we met:
_____
_____

Best story told:
_____
_____

The kids liked this:
_____
_____

The best food:
_____
_____

Games played:
_____
_____

Something disappointing:
_____
_____

Next time I'll do this differently:
_____
_____

Fahnestock State Park
City: Carmel   County: Putnam

Plan your trip: https://parks.ny.gov/parks/fahnestock/details.aspx

Activities:

- ❑ Biking
- ❑ Boating
- ❑ Canoeing
- ❑ Disc Golf
- ❑ Fishing / Ice
- ❑ Hiking
- ❑ Horseback Riding
- ❑ Hunting
- ❑ Kayaking
- ❑ Marina
- ❑ Nature Center / Trails

- ❑ Photography
- ❑ Playing Fields
- ❑ Scenic Views
- ❑ Swimming
- ❑ Waterfalls
- ❑ Wildlife & Birding
- ❑ Winter Sports
- ❑
- ❑
- ❑
- ❑

Facilities:

- ❑ ADA
- ❑ Picnic sites
- ❑ Restrooms
- ❑ Showers
- ❑ Trailer Access
- ❑ Visitor center

- ❑ Group Camping
- ❑ RV Camp
- ❑ Rustic Camping
- ❑ Cabins / Yurts
- ❑ Day Use Area
- ❑

Notes:

Get the Facts

- ❑ Phone   (845) 225-7207
- ❑ Park Hours

   _____

- ❑ Reservations? ____Y ____N

   date made_____
- ❑ Open all year ____Y____N

   dates_____
- ❑ Check in time _____
- ❑ Check out time _____
- ❑ Pet friendly _____Y _____N
- ❑ Max RV length _____
- ❑ Distance from home

   miles: _____

   hours: _____
- ❑ Address_____

   _____

   _____

Fees:

- ❑ Day Use $ _____
- ❑ Camp Sites $ _____
- ❑ RV Sites $ _____
- ❑ Refund policy

   _____

   _____

   _____

Make It Personal

Trip dates: _____ | The weather was: Sunny Cloudy Rainy Stormy Snowy Foggy Warm Cold

Why I went:
_____

_____

How I got there: (circle all that apply) Plane Train Car Bus Bike Hike RV MC
_____

I went with:
_____

We stayed in (space, cabin # etc):
_____

Most relaxing day:
_____

_____

Something funny:
_____

_____

Someone we met:
_____

_____

Best story told:
_____

_____

The kids liked this:
_____

_____

The best food:
_____

_____

Games played:
_____

_____

Something disappointing:
_____

_____

Next time I'll do this differently:
_____

_____

Wonder Lake State Park
City: Holmes   County: Dutchess

Plan your trip: https://parks.ny.gov/parks/wonderlake/details.aspx

Activities: (check all that apply)

- ❑ Beach
- ❑ Biking
- ❑ Boating
- ❑ Canoeing
- ❑ Fishing / Ice
- ❑ Hiking
- ❑ Horseback Riding
- ❑ Hunting
- ❑ Kayaking

- ❑ Marina
- ❑ Nature Center
- ❑ Photography
- ❑ Swimming
- ❑ Waterfalls
- ❑ Watersports
- ❑ Wildlife & Birding
- ❑ Winter Sports
- ❑

Facilities:

- ❑ ADA
- ❑ Gift Shop
- ❑ Museum
- ❑ Visitor Center
- ❑ Restrooms

- ❑ Playground
- ❑ Picnic sites
- ❑
- ❑
- ❑

Memories of the Trip

Get the Facts

- ❑ Phone   (845) 225-7207
- ❑ Park Hours

_____

- ❑ Reservations? ____Y ____N

date made_____

- ❑ Open all year? ____Y____N

dates_____

- ❑ Dog friendly _____Y _____N
- ❑ Distance from home

miles: _____

hours: _____

- ❑ Address_____

_____

_____

Fees:

- ❑ Day Use $ _____
- ❑ Refund policy

_____

_____

_____

Stamps & Stickers

James Baird State Park
City: Pleasant Valley   County: Dutchess

Plan your trip: https://parks.ny.gov/parks/jamesbaird/details.aspx

Activities: (check all that apply)

- ❑ Beach
- ❑ Biking
- ❑ Boating
- ❑ Canoeing
- ❑ Fishing / Ice
- ❑ Hiking
- ❑ Horseback Riding
- ❑ Hunting
- ❑ Kayaking

- ❑ Marina
- ❑ Nature Center
- ❑ Photography
- ❑ Swimming
- ❑ Waterfalls
- ❑ Watersports
- ❑ Wildlife & Birding
- ❑ Winter Sports
- ❑

Facilities:

- ❑ ADA
- ❑ Gift Shop
- ❑ Museum
- ❑ Visitor Center
- ❑ Restrooms

- ❑ Playground
- ❑ Picnic sites
- ❑
- ❑
- ❑

Memories of the Trip

Get the Facts

- ❑ Phone   (845) 452-1489
- ❑ Park Hours

    _____

- ❑ Reservations? _____ Y _____ N

    date made_____

- ❑ Open all year? _____ Y _____ N

    dates_____

- ❑ Dog friendly _____ Y _____ N

- ❑ Distance from home

    miles: _____

    hours: _____

- ❑ Address_____

    _____

    _____

Fees:

- ❑ Day Use $ _____
- ❑ Refund policy

    _____

    _____

    _____

Stamps & Stickers

Ogden Mills & Ruth Livingston Mills State Park

City: Staatsburg County: Dutchess

Plan your trip: https://parks.ny.gov/parks/33/details.aspx

Activities: (check all that apply)

- ❏ Beach
- ❏ Biking
- ❏ Boating
- ❏ Canoeing
- ❏ Fishing / Ice
- ❏ Hiking
- ❏ Horseback Riding
- ❏ Hunting
- ❏ Kayaking

- ❏ Marina
- ❏ Nature Center
- ❏ Photography
- ❏ Swimming
- ❏ Waterfalls
- ❏ Watersports
- ❏ Wildlife & Birding
- ❏ Winter Sports
- ❏

Facilities:

- ❏ ADA
- ❏ Gift Shop
- ❏ Museum
- ❏ Visitor Center
- ❏ Restrooms

- ❏ Playground
- ❏ Picnic sites
- ❏
- ❏
- ❏

Memories of the Trip

Get the Facts

- ❏ Phone   (845) 889-4646
- ❏ Park Hours

  _____

- ❏ Reservations? ____Y ____N

  date made_____

- ❏ Open all year? ____Y____N

  dates_____

- ❏ Dog friendly _____Y _____N

- ❏ Distance from home

  miles: _____

  hours: _____

- ❏ Address_____

  _____

  _____

Fees:

- ❏ Day Use $ _____
- ❏ Refund policy

  _____

  _____

  _____

Stamps & Stickers

Fahnestock Winter Park
City: Carmel   County: Putnam

Plan your trip: https://parks.ny.gov/parks/fahnestockwinterpark/details.aspx

Activities: (check all that apply)

- ❏ Beach
- ❏ Biking
- ❏ Boating
- ❏ Canoeing
- ❏ Fishing / Ice
- ❏ Hiking
- ❏ Horseback Riding
- ❏ Hunting
- ❏ Kayaking

- ❏ Marina
- ❏ Nature Center
- ❏ Photography
- ❏ Swimming
- ❏ Waterfalls
- ❏ Watersports
- ❏ Wildlife & Birding
- ❏ Winter Sports
- ❏

Facilities:

- ❏ ADA
- ❏ Gift Shop
- ❏ Museum
- ❏ Visitor Center
- ❏ Restrooms

- ❏ Playground
- ❏ Picnic sites
- ❏
- ❏
- ❏

Memories of the Trip

Get the Facts

- ❏ Phone   (845) 225-3998
- ❏ Park Hours

  _____

- ❏ Reservations? ____Y ____N

  date made_____

- ❏ Open all year? ____Y____N

  dates_____

- ❏ Dog friendly _____Y _____N

- ❏ Distance from home

  miles: _____

  hours: _____

- ❏ Address_____

  _____

  _____

Fees:

- ❏ Day Use $ _____
- ❏ Refund policy

  _____

  _____

  _____

Stamps & Stickers

Hudson Highlands State Park Preserve
City: Cold Spring   County: Putnam

Plan your trip: https://parks.ny.gov/parks/hudsonhighlands/details.aspx

Activities: (check all that apply)

- ❑ Beach
- ❑ Biking
- ❑ Boating
- ❑ Canoeing
- ❑ Fishing / Ice
- ❑ Hiking
- ❑ Horseback Riding
- ❑ Hunting
- ❑ Kayaking

- ❑ Marina
- ❑ Nature Center
- ❑ Photography
- ❑ Swimming
- ❑ Waterfalls
- ❑ Watersports
- ❑ Wildlife & Birding
- ❑ Winter Sports
- ❑

Facilities:

- ❑ ADA
- ❑ Gift Shop
- ❑ Museum
- ❑ Visitor Center
- ❑ Restrooms

- ❑ Playground
- ❑ Picnic sites
- ❑
- ❑
- ❑

Memories of the Trip

Get the Facts

- ❑ Phone   (845) 265-3175
- ❑ Park Hours

_____

- ❑ Reservations? ____Y ____N

date made_____

- ❑ Open all year? ____Y____N

dates_____

- ❑ Dog friendly _____Y _____N
- ❑ Distance from home

miles: _____

hours: _____

- ❑ Address_____

_____

_____

Fees:

- ❑ Day Use $ _____
- ❑ Refund policy

_____

_____

_____

Stamps & Stickers

Rockefeller State Park Preserve
City: Pleasantville   County: Westchester

Plan your trip: https://parks.ny.gov/parks/rockefeller/details.aspx

Activities: (check all that apply)

- ❑ Beach
- ❑ Biking
- ❑ Boating
- ❑ Canoeing
- ❑ Fishing / Ice
- ❑ Hiking
- ❑ Horseback Riding
- ❑ Hunting
- ❑ Kayaking

- ❑ Marina
- ❑ Nature Center
- ❑ Photography
- ❑ Swimming
- ❑ Waterfalls
- ❑ Watersports
- ❑ Wildlife & Birding
- ❑ Winter Sports
- ❑

Facilities:

- ❑ ADA
- ❑ Gift Shop
- ❑ Museum
- ❑ Visitor Center
- ❑ Restrooms

- ❑ Playground
- ❑ Picnic sites
- ❑
- ❑
- ❑

Memories of the Trip

Get the Facts

- ❑ Phone   (914) 631-1470
- ❑ Park Hours

  _____

- ❑ Reservations? _____ Y _____ N

  date made_____

- ❑ Open all year? _____ Y _____ N

  dates_____

- ❑ Dog friendly _____ Y _____ N

- ❑ Distance from home

  miles: _____

  hours: _____

- ❑ Address_____

  _____

  _____

Fees:

- ❑ Day Use $ _____
- ❑ Refund policy

  _____

  _____

Stamps & Stickers

Franklin D. Roosevelt State Park
City: Yorktown Heights   County: Westchester

Plan your trip: https://parks.ny.gov/parks/franklinroosevelt/details.aspx

Activities: (check all that apply)

- ❑ Beach
- ❑ Biking
- ❑ Boating
- ❑ Canoeing
- ❑ Fishing / Ice
- ❑ Hiking
- ❑ Horseback Riding
- ❑ Hunting
- ❑ Kayaking

- ❑ Marina
- ❑ Nature Center
- ❑ Photography
- ❑ Swimming
- ❑ Waterfalls
- ❑ Watersports
- ❑ Wildlife & Birding
- ❑ Winter Sports
- ❑

Facilities:

- ❑ ADA
- ❑ Gift Shop
- ❑ Museum
- ❑ Visitor Center
- ❑ Restrooms

- ❑ Playground
- ❑ Picnic sites
- ❑
- ❑
- ❑

Memories of the Trip

Get the Facts

- ❑ Phone   (914) 245-4434
- ❑ Park Hours

_____

- ❑ Reservations? _____Y _____N

date made_____

- ❑ Open all year? _____Y_____N

dates_____

- ❑ Dog friendly _____Y _____N
- ❑ Distance from home

miles: _____

hours: _____

- ❑ Address_____

_____

_____

Fees:

- ❑ Day Use $ _____
- ❑ Refund policy

_____

_____

_____

Stamps & Stickers

Long Island & NYC Region

- Bronx County
- Kings County
- Nassau County
- New York County
- Queens County
- Richmond County
- Suffolk County

Heckscher State Park
City: East Islip   County: Suffolk

Plan your trip: https://parks.ny.gov/parks/heckscher/details.aspx

Activities:

- ❏ Biking
- ❏ Boating
- ❏ Canoeing
- ❏ Disc Golf
- ❏ Fishing / Ice
- ❏ Hiking
- ❏ Horseback Riding
- ❏ Hunting
- ❏ Kayaking
- ❏ Marina
- ❏ Nature Center / Trails
- ❏ Photography
- ❏ Playing Fields
- ❏ Scenic Views
- ❏ Swimming
- ❏ Waterfalls
- ❏ Wildlife & Birding
- ❏ Winter Sports
- ❏
- ❏
- ❏
- ❏

Facilities:

- ❏ ADA
- ❏ Picnic sites
- ❏ Restrooms
- ❏ Showers
- ❏ Trailer Access
- ❏ Visitor center
- ❏ Group Camping
- ❏ RV Camp
- ❏ Rustic Camping
- ❏ Cabins / Yurts
- ❏ Day Use Area
- ❏

Notes:

Get the Facts

- ❏ Phone (631) 581-2100
- ❏ Park Hours

  _____

- ❏ Reservations? ____Y ____N

  date made_____

- ❏ Open all year ____Y____N

  dates_____

- ❏ Check in time _____
- ❏ Check out time _____
- ❏ Pet friendly _____Y _____N
- ❏ Max RV length _____
- ❏ Distance from home

  miles: _____

  hours: _____

- ❏ Address_____

  _____

  _____

Fees:

- ❏ Day Use $ _____
- ❏ Camp Sites $ _____
- ❏ RV Sites $ _____
- ❏ Refund policy

  _____

  _____

  _____

Make It Personal

Trip dates: _____ | The weather was: Sunny Cloudy Rainy Stormy Snowy Foggy Warm Cold

Why I went: _____

_____

How I got there: (circle all that apply)   Plane   Train   Car   Bus   Bike   Hike   RV   MC

I went with: _____

We stayed in (space, cabin # etc): _____

Most relaxing day: _____

_____

Something funny: _____

_____

Someone we met: _____

_____

Best story told: _____

_____

The kids liked this: _____

_____

The best food: _____

_____

Games played: _____

_____

Something disappointing: _____

_____

Next time I'll do this differently: _____

_____

Hither Hills State Park

City: Montauk   County: Suffolk

Plan your trip: https://parks.ny.gov/parks/hitherhills/details.aspx

Activities:

- ☐ Biking
- ☐ Boating
- ☐ Canoeing
- ☐ Disc Golf
- ☐ Fishing / Ice
- ☐ Hiking
- ☐ Horseback Riding
- ☐ Hunting
- ☐ Kayaking
- ☐ Marina
- ☐ Nature Center / Trails
- ☐ Photography
- ☐ Playing Fields
- ☐ Scenic Views
- ☐ Swimming
- ☐ Waterfalls
- ☐ Wildlife & Birding
- ☐ Winter Sports
- ☐
- ☐
- ☐
- ☐

Facilities:

- ☐ ADA
- ☐ Picnic sites
- ☐ Restrooms
- ☐ Showers
- ☐ Trailer Access
- ☐ Visitor center
- ☐ Group Camping
- ☐ RV Camp
- ☐ Rustic Camping
- ☐ Cabins / Yurts
- ☐ Day Use Area
- ☐

Notes:

Get the Facts

- ☐ Phone   (631) 668-2554
- ☐ Park Hours

  _____

- ☐ Reservations? _____Y _____N

  date made_____

- ☐ Open all year _____Y_____N

  dates_____

- ☐ Check in time _____
- ☐ Check out time _____
- ☐ Pet friendly _____Y _____N
- ☐ Max RV length _____
- ☐ Distance from home

  miles: _____

  hours: _____

- ☐ Address_____

  _____

  _____

Fees:

- ☐ Day Use $ _____
- ☐ Camp Sites $ _____
- ☐ RV Sites $ _____
- ☐ Refund policy

  _____

  _____

  _____

Make It Personal

Trip dates: _____ | The weather was: Sunny   Cloudy   Rainy   Stormy   Snowy   Foggy   Warm   Cold

Why I went:
_____
_____

How I got there: (circle all that apply)   Plane   Train   Car   Bus   Bike   Hike   RV   MC
_____

I went with:
_____

We stayed in (space, cabin # etc):
_____

Most relaxing day:
_____
_____

Something funny:
_____
_____

Someone we met:
_____
_____

Best story told:
_____
_____

The kids liked this:
_____
_____

The best food:
_____
_____

Games played:
_____
_____

Something disappointing:
_____
_____

Next time I'll do this differently:
_____
_____

Wildwood State Park
City: Wading River   County: Suffolk

Plan your trip: https://parks.ny.gov/parks/wildwood/details.aspx

Activities:

- ❑ Biking
- ❑ Boating
- ❑ Canoeing
- ❑ Disc Golf
- ❑ Fishing / Ice
- ❑ Hiking
- ❑ Horseback Riding
- ❑ Hunting
- ❑ Kayaking
- ❑ Marina
- ❑ Nature Center / Trails

- ❑ Photography
- ❑ Playing Fields
- ❑ Scenic Views
- ❑ Swimming
- ❑ Waterfalls
- ❑ Wildlife & Birding
- ❑ Winter Sports
- ❑
- ❑
- ❑
- ❑

Facilities:

- ❑ ADA
- ❑ Picnic sites
- ❑ Restrooms
- ❑ Showers
- ❑ Trailer Access
- ❑ Visitor center

- ❑ Group Camping
- ❑ RV Camp
- ❑ Rustic Camping
- ❑ Cabins / Yurts
- ❑ Day Use Area
- ❑

Notes:

Get the Facts

- ❑ Phone   (631) 929-4314
- ❑ Park Hours

  _____
- ❑ Reservations? ____Y ____N

  date made_____
- ❑ Open all year ____Y_____N

  dates_____
- ❑ Check in time _____
- ❑ Check out time _____
- ❑ Pet friendly _____Y _____N
- ❑ Max RV length _____
- ❑ Distance from home

  miles: _____

  hours: _____
- ❑ Address_____

  _____

  _____

Fees:

- ❑ Day Use $ _____
- ❑ Camp Sites $ _____
- ❑ RV Sites $ _____
- ❑ Refund policy

  _____

  _____

  _____

Make It Personal

Trip dates: _____ | The weather was: Sunny Cloudy Rainy Stormy Snowy Foggy Warm Cold

Why I went:
_____
_____

How I got there: (circle all that apply) Plane Train Car Bus Bike Hike RV MC
_____

I went with:
_____

We stayed in (space, cabin # etc):
_____

Most relaxing day:
_____
_____

Something funny:
_____
_____

Someone we met:
_____
_____

Best story told:
_____
_____

The kids liked this:
_____
_____

The best food:
_____
_____

Games played:
_____
_____

Something disappointing:
_____
_____

Next time I'll do this differently:
_____
_____

Roberto Clemente State Park
City: Bronx   County: Bronx

Plan your trip: https://parks.ny.gov/parks/robertoclemente/details.aspx

Activities: (check all that apply)

- ❏ Beach
- ❏ Biking
- ❏ Boating
- ❏ Canoeing
- ❏ Fishing / Ice
- ❏ Hiking
- ❏ Horseback Riding
- ❏ Hunting
- ❏ Kayaking

- ❏ Marina
- ❏ Nature Center
- ❏ Photography
- ❏ Swimming
- ❏ Waterfalls
- ❏ Watersports
- ❏ Wildlife & Birding
- ❏ Winter Sports
- ❏

Facilities:

- ❏ ADA
- ❏ Gift Shop
- ❏ Museum
- ❏ Visitor Center
- ❏ Restrooms

- ❏ Playground
- ❏ Picnic sites
- ❏
- ❏
- ❏

Memories of the Trip

Get the Facts

- ❏ Phone   (718) 299-8750
- ❏ Park Hours

  _____

- ❏ Reservations? ____Y ____N

  date made_____

- ❏ Open all year? ____Y____N

  dates_____

- ❏ Dog friendly _____Y _____N

- ❏ Distance from home

  miles: _____

  hours: _____

- ❏ Address_____

  _____

  _____

Fees:

- ❏ Day Use $ _____
- ❏ Refund policy

  _____

  _____

  _____

Stamps & Stickers

Marsha P. Johnson State Park
City: Brooklyn   County: Kings
Plan your trip: https://parks.ny.gov/parks/eastriver/details.aspx

Activities: (check all that apply)

- ❑ Beach
- ❑ Biking
- ❑ Boating
- ❑ Canoeing
- ❑ Fishing / Ice
- ❑ Hiking
- ❑ Horseback Riding
- ❑ Hunting
- ❑ Kayaking

- ❑ Marina
- ❑ Nature Center
- ❑ Photography
- ❑ Swimming
- ❑ Waterfalls
- ❑ Watersports
- ❑ Wildlife & Birding
- ❑ Winter Sports
- ❑

Facilities:

- ❑ ADA
- ❑ Gift Shop
- ❑ Museum
- ❑ Visitor Center
- ❑ Restrooms

- ❑ Playground
- ❑ Picnic sites
- ❑
- ❑
- ❑

Memories of the Trip

Get the Facts

- ❑ Phone   (718) 782-2731
- ❑ Park Hours

  _____

- ❑ Reservations? ____Y ____N

  date made_____

- ❑ Open all year? ____Y____N

  dates_____

- ❑ Dog friendly ____Y ____N

- ❑ Distance from home

  miles: _____

  hours: _____

- ❑ Address_____

  _____

  _____

Fees:

- ❑ Day Use $ _____
- ❑ Refund policy

  _____

  _____

  _____

Stamps & Stickers

Shirley Chisholm State Park
City: Brooklyn   County: Kings

Plan your trip: https://parks.ny.gov/parks/shirleychisholm/details.aspx

Activities: (check all that apply)

- ❑ Beach
- ❑ Biking
- ❑ Boating
- ❑ Canoeing
- ❑ Fishing / Ice
- ❑ Hiking
- ❑ Horseback Riding
- ❑ Hunting
- ❑ Kayaking

- ❑ Marina
- ❑ Nature Center
- ❑ Photography
- ❑ Swimming
- ❑ Waterfalls
- ❑ Watersports
- ❑ Wildlife & Birding
- ❑ Winter Sports
- ❑

Facilities:

- ❑ ADA
- ❑ Gift Shop
- ❑ Museum
- ❑ Visitor Center
- ❑ Restrooms

- ❑ Playground
- ❑ Picnic sites
- ❑
- ❑
- ❑

Memories of the Trip

Get the Facts

- ❑ Phone   (718) 277-2420
- ❑ Park Hours

_____

- ❑ Reservations? _____Y _____N

date made_____

- ❑ Open all year? _____Y_____N

dates_____

- ❑ Dog friendly _____Y _____N
- ❑ Distance from home

miles: _____

hours: _____

- ❑ Address_____

_____

_____

Fees:

- ❑ Day Use $ _____
- ❑ Refund policy

_____

_____

_____

Stamps & Stickers

Bethpage State Park
City: Farmingdale   County: Nassau

Plan your trip: https://parks.ny.gov/parks/bethpage/details.aspx

Activities: (check all that apply)

❑ Beach
❑ Biking
❑ Boating
❑ Canoeing
❑ Fishing / Ice
❑ Hiking
❑ Horseback Riding
❑ Hunting
❑ Kayaking

❑ Marina
❑ Nature Center
❑ Photography
❑ Swimming
❑ Waterfalls
❑ Watersports
❑ Wildlife & Birding
❑ Winter Sports
❑

Facilities:

❑ ADA
❑ Gift Shop
❑ Museum
❑ Visitor Center
❑ Restrooms

❑ Playground
❑ Picnic sites
❑
❑
❑

Memories of the Trip

Get the Facts

❑ Phone   (516) 249-0701
❑ Park Hours

_____

❑ Reservations? ____Y ____N

date made_____

❑ Open all year? ____Y____N

dates_____

❑ Dog friendly _____Y _____N

❑ Distance from home

miles: _____

hours: _____

❑ Address_____

_____

_____

Fees:

❑ Day Use $ _____
❑ Refund policy

_____

_____

_____

Stamps & Stickers

Valley Stream State Park
City: Valley Stream   County: Nassau

Plan your trip: https://parks.ny.gov/parks/valleystream/details.aspx

Activities: (check all that apply)

- ❑ Beach
- ❑ Biking
- ❑ Boating
- ❑ Canoeing
- ❑ Fishing / Ice
- ❑ Hiking
- ❑ Horseback Riding
- ❑ Hunting
- ❑ Kayaking

- ❑ Marina
- ❑ Nature Center
- ❑ Photography
- ❑ Swimming
- ❑ Waterfalls
- ❑ Watersports
- ❑ Wildlife & Birding
- ❑ Winter Sports
- ❑

Facilities:

- ❑ ADA
- ❑ Gift Shop
- ❑ Museum
- ❑ Visitor Center
- ❑ Restrooms

- ❑ Playground
- ❑ Picnic sites
- ❑
- ❑
- ❑

Memories of the Trip

Get the Facts

- ❑ Phone   (516) 825-4128
- ❑ Park Hours

  _____

- ❑ Reservations? ____Y ____N

  date made_____

- ❑ Open all year? ____Y____N

  dates_____

- ❑ Dog friendly _____Y _____N

- ❑ Distance from home

  miles: _____

  hours: _____

- ❑ Address_____

  _____

  _____

Fees:

- ❑ Day Use $ _____
- ❑ Refund policy

  _____

  _____

  _____

Stamps & Stickers

Jones Beach State Park

City: Wantagh   County: Nassau

Plan your trip: https://parks.ny.gov/parks/jonesbeach/details.aspx

Activities: (check all that apply)

- ❑ Beach
- ❑ Biking
- ❑ Boating
- ❑ Canoeing
- ❑ Fishing / Ice
- ❑ Hiking
- ❑ Horseback Riding
- ❑ Hunting
- ❑ Kayaking

- ❑ Marina
- ❑ Nature Center
- ❑ Photography
- ❑ Swimming
- ❑ Waterfalls
- ❑ Watersports
- ❑ Wildlife & Birding
- ❑ Winter Sports
- ❑

Facilities:

- ❑ ADA
- ❑ Gift Shop
- ❑ Museum
- ❑ Visitor Center
- ❑ Restrooms

- ❑ Playground
- ❑ Picnic sites
- ❑
- ❑
- ❑

Memories of the Trip

Get the Facts

- ❑ Phone   (516) 785-1600
- ❑ Park Hours

   _____

- ❑ Reservations? _____Y _____N

date made_____

- ❑ Open all year? _____Y_____N

dates_____

- ❑ Dog friendly _____Y _____N

- ❑ Distance from home

miles: _____

hours: _____

- ❑ Address_____

   _____

   _____

Fees:

- ❑ Day Use $ _____
- ❑ Refund policy

   _____

   _____

   _____

Stamps & Stickers

Hempstead Lake State Park
City: West Hempstead   County: Nassau

Plan your trip: https://parks.ny.gov/parks/hempsteadlake/details.aspx

Activities: (check all that apply)

- ❑ Beach
- ❑ Biking
- ❑ Boating
- ❑ Canoeing
- ❑ Fishing / Ice
- ❑ Hiking
- ❑ Horseback Riding
- ❑ Hunting
- ❑ Kayaking

- ❑ Marina
- ❑ Nature Center
- ❑ Photography
- ❑ Swimming
- ❑ Waterfalls
- ❑ Watersports
- ❑ Wildlife & Birding
- ❑ Winter Sports
- ❑

Facilities:

- ❑ ADA
- ❑ Gift Shop
- ❑ Museum
- ❑ Visitor Center
- ❑ Restrooms

- ❑ Playground
- ❑ Picnic sites
- ❑
- ❑
- ❑

Memories of the Trip

Get the Facts

- ❑ Phone   (516) 766-1029
- ❑ Park Hours

  _____

- ❑ Reservations? ____Y ____N

  date made_____
- ❑ Open all year? ____Y____N

  dates_____
- ❑ Dog friendly _____Y _____N
- ❑ Distance from home

  miles: _____

  hours: _____
- ❑ Address_____

  _____

  _____

Fees:

- ❑ Day Use $ _____
- ❑ Refund policy

  _____

  _____

  _____

Stamps & Stickers

Trail View State Park
City: Woodbury   County: Nassau

Plan your trip: https://parks.ny.gov/parks/trailview/details.aspx

Activities: (check all that apply)

- ❑ Beach
- ❑ Biking
- ❑ Boating
- ❑ Canoeing
- ❑ Fishing / Ice
- ❑ Hiking
- ❑ Horseback Riding
- ❑ Hunting
- ❑ Kayaking

- ❑ Marina
- ❑ Nature Center
- ❑ Photography
- ❑ Swimming
- ❑ Waterfalls
- ❑ Watersports
- ❑ Wildlife & Birding
- ❑ Winter Sports
- ❑

Facilities:

- ❑ ADA
- ❑ Gift Shop
- ❑ Museum
- ❑ Visitor Center
- ❑ Restrooms

- ❑ Playground
- ❑ Picnic sites
- ❑
- ❑
- ❑

Memories of the Trip

Get the Facts

- ❑ Phone   (631) 423-1770
- ❑ Park Hours

_____

- ❑ Reservations? ____Y ____N

date made_____

- ❑ Open all year? ____Y____N

dates_____

- ❑ Dog friendly _____Y _____N
- ❑ Distance from home

miles: _____

hours: _____

- ❑ Address_____

_____

_____

Fees:

- ❑ Day Use $ _____
- ❑ Refund policy

_____

_____

_____

Stamps & Stickers

Franklin D. Roosevelt Four Freedoms State Park

City: New York   County: New York

Plan your trip: https://parks.ny.gov/parks/fdrfourfreedoms/details.aspx

Activities: (check all that apply)

- ❑ Beach
- ❑ Biking
- ❑ Boating
- ❑ Canoeing
- ❑ Fishing / Ice
- ❑ Hiking
- ❑ Horseback Riding
- ❑ Hunting
- ❑ Kayaking

- ❑ Marina
- ❑ Nature Center
- ❑ Photography
- ❑ Swimming
- ❑ Waterfalls
- ❑ Watersports
- ❑ Wildlife & Birding
- ❑ Winter Sports
- ❑

Facilities:

- ❑ ADA
- ❑ Gift Shop
- ❑ Museum
- ❑ Visitor Center
- ❑ Restrooms

- ❑ Playground
- ❑ Picnic sites
- ❑
- ❑
- ❑

Memories of the Trip

Get the Facts

- ❑ Phone   (212) 204-8831
- ❑ Park Hours

  _____

- ❑ Reservations? ____Y ____N

  date made_____

- ❑ Open all year? ____Y____N

  dates_____

- ❑ Dog friendly _____Y _____N
- ❑ Distance from home

  miles: _____

  hours: _____

- ❑ Address_____

  _____

  _____

Fees:

- ❑ Day Use $ _____
- ❑ Refund policy

  _____

  _____

  _____

Stamps & Stickers

Hudson River Park
City: New York   County: New York
Plan your trip: https://parks.ny.gov/parks/hudsonriverpark/details.aspx

Activities: (check all that apply)

- ❏ Beach
- ❏ Biking
- ❏ Boating
- ❏ Canoeing
- ❏ Fishing / Ice
- ❏ Hiking
- ❏ Horseback Riding
- ❏ Hunting
- ❏ Kayaking

- ❏ Marina
- ❏ Nature Center
- ❏ Photography
- ❏ Swimming
- ❏ Waterfalls
- ❏ Watersports
- ❏ Wildlife & Birding
- ❏ Winter Sports
- ❏

Facilities:

- ❏ ADA
- ❏ Gift Shop
- ❏ Museum
- ❏ Visitor Center
- ❏ Restrooms

- ❏ Playground
- ❏ Picnic sites
- ❏
- ❏
- ❏

Memories of the Trip

Get the Facts

- ❏ Phone   (212) 627-2020
- ❏ Park Hours

_____

- ❏ Reservations? ____Y ____N

  date made_____

- ❏ Open all year? ____Y____N

  dates_____

- ❏ Dog friendly _____Y _____N

- ❏ Distance from home

  miles: _____

  hours: _____

- ❏ Address_____

  _____

  _____

Fees:

- ❏ Day Use $ _____
- ❏ Refund policy

  _____

  _____

  _____

Stamps & Stickers

Riverbank State Park
City: New York   County: New York

Plan your trip: https://parks.ny.gov/parks/riverbank/details.aspx

Activities: (check all that apply)

- ❏ Beach
- ❏ Biking
- ❏ Boating
- ❏ Canoeing
- ❏ Fishing / Ice
- ❏ Hiking
- ❏ Horseback Riding
- ❏ Hunting
- ❏ Kayaking

- ❏ Marina
- ❏ Nature Center
- ❏ Photography
- ❏ Swimming
- ❏ Waterfalls
- ❏ Watersports
- ❏ Wildlife & Birding
- ❏ Winter Sports
- ❏

Facilities:

- ❏ ADA
- ❏ Gift Shop
- ❏ Museum
- ❏ Visitor Center
- ❏ Restrooms

- ❏ Playground
- ❏ Picnic sites
- ❏
- ❏
- ❏

Memories of the Trip

Get the Facts

- ❏ Phone   (212) 694-3600
- ❏ Park Hours

_____

- ❏ Reservations? _____Y _____N

date made_____

- ❏ Open all year? _____Y_____N

dates_____

- ❏ Dog friendly _____Y _____N
- ❏ Distance from home

miles: _____

hours: _____

- ❏ Address_____

_____

_____

Fees:

- ❏ Day Use $ _____
- ❏ Refund policy

_____

_____

_____

Stamps & Stickers

Bayswater Point State Park
City: Far Rockaway   County: Queens

Plan your trip: https://parks.ny.gov/parks/bayswaterpoint/details.aspx

Activities: (check all that apply)

- ❑ Beach
- ❑ Biking
- ❑ Boating
- ❑ Canoeing
- ❑ Fishing / Ice
- ❑ Hiking
- ❑ Horseback Riding
- ❑ Hunting
- ❑ Kayaking

- ❑ Marina
- ❑ Nature Center
- ❑ Photography
- ❑ Swimming
- ❑ Waterfalls
- ❑ Watersports
- ❑ Wildlife & Birding
- ❑ Winter Sports
- ❑

Facilities:

- ❑ ADA
- ❑ Gift Shop
- ❑ Museum
- ❑ Visitor Center
- ❑ Restrooms

- ❑ Playground
- ❑ Picnic sites
- ❑
- ❑
- ❑

Memories of the Trip

Get the Facts

- ❑ Phone   (718) 471-1018
- ❑ Park Hours

  _____

- ❑ Reservations? ____Y ____N

  date made_____

- ❑ Open all year? ____Y____N

  dates_____

- ❑ Dog friendly _____Y _____N

- ❑ Distance from home

  miles: _____

  hours: _____

- ❑ Address_____

  _____

  _____

Fees:

- ❑ Day Use $ _____
- ❑ Refund policy

  _____

  _____

  _____

Stamps & Stickers

Gantry Plaza State Park
City: Long Island City   County: Queens

Plan your trip: https://parks.ny.gov/parks/gantryplaza/details.aspx

Activities: (check all that apply)

- ❏ Beach
- ❏ Biking
- ❏ Boating
- ❏ Canoeing
- ❏ Fishing / Ice
- ❏ Hiking
- ❏ Horseback Riding
- ❏ Hunting
- ❏ Kayaking

- ❏ Marina
- ❏ Nature Center
- ❏ Photography
- ❏ Swimming
- ❏ Waterfalls
- ❏ Watersports
- ❏ Wildlife & Birding
- ❏ Winter Sports
- ❏

Facilities:

- ❏ ADA
- ❏ Gift Shop
- ❏ Museum
- ❏ Visitor Center
- ❏ Restrooms

- ❏ Playground
- ❏ Picnic sites
- ❏
- ❏
- ❏

Memories of the Trip

Get the Facts

- ❏ Phone   (718) 786-6385
- ❏ Park Hours

  _____

- ❏ Reservations? _____Y _____N

  date made_____

- ❏ Open all year? _____Y_____N

  dates_____

- ❏ Dog friendly _____Y _____N

- ❏ Distance from home

  miles: _____

  hours: _____

- ❏ Address_____

  _____

  _____

Fees:

- ❏ Day Use $ _____
- ❏ Refund policy

  _____

  _____

  _____

Stamps & Stickers

Clay Pit Ponds State Park Preserve
City: Staten Island   County: Richmond

Plan your trip: https://parks.ny.gov/parks/claypitponds/details.aspx

Activities: (check all that apply)

- ❑ Beach
- ❑ Biking
- ❑ Boating
- ❑ Canoeing
- ❑ Fishing / Ice
- ❑ Hiking
- ❑ Horseback Riding
- ❑ Hunting
- ❑ Kayaking

- ❑ Marina
- ❑ Nature Center
- ❑ Photography
- ❑ Swimming
- ❑ Waterfalls
- ❑ Watersports
- ❑ Wildlife & Birding
- ❑ Winter Sports
- ❑

Facilities:

- ❑ ADA
- ❑ Gift Shop
- ❑ Museum
- ❑ Visitor Center
- ❑ Restrooms

- ❑ Playground
- ❑ Picnic sites
- ❑
- ❑
- ❑

Get the Facts

- ❑ Phone   (718) 967-1976
- ❑ Park Hours

  _____

- ❑ Reservations? _____Y _____N

  date made_____

- ❑ Open all year? _____Y_____N

  dates_____

- ❑ Dog friendly _____Y _____N

- ❑ Distance from home

  miles: _____

  hours: _____

- ❑ Address_____

  _____

  _____

Fees:

- ❑ Day Use $ _____
- ❑ Refund policy

  _____

  _____

  _____

Stamps & Stickers

Memories of the Trip

Gilgo State Park
City: Babylon   County: Suffolk

Plan your trip: https://parks.ny.gov/parks/gilgo/details.aspx

Activities: (check all that apply)

- ❑ Beach
- ❑ Biking
- ❑ Boating
- ❑ Canoeing
- ❑ Fishing / Ice
- ❑ Hiking
- ❑ Horseback Riding
- ❑ Hunting
- ❑ Kayaking

- ❑ Marina
- ❑ Nature Center
- ❑ Photography
- ❑ Swimming
- ❑ Waterfalls
- ❑ Watersports
- ❑ Wildlife & Birding
- ❑ Winter Sports
- ❑

Facilities:

- ❑ ADA
- ❑ Gift Shop
- ❑ Museum
- ❑ Visitor Center
- ❑ Restrooms

- ❑ Playground
- ❑ Picnic sites
- ❑
- ❑
- ❑

Memories of the Trip

Get the Facts

- ❑ Phone   (631) 826-1255
- ❑ Park Hours

_____

- ❑ Reservations? ____ Y ____ N

date made_____

- ❑ Open all year? ____ Y ____ N

dates_____

- ❑ Dog friendly ____ Y ____ N
- ❑ Distance from home

miles: _____

hours: _____

- ❑ Address_____

_____

_____

Fees:

- ❑ Day Use $ _____
- ❑ Refund policy

_____

_____

_____

Stamps & Stickers

Robert Moses State Park-Long Island
City: Babylon   County: Suffolk

Plan your trip: https://parks.ny.gov/parks/robertmoses/details.aspx

Activities: (check all that apply)

- ☐ Beach
- ☐ Biking
- ☐ Boating
- ☐ Canoeing
- ☐ Fishing / Ice
- ☐ Hiking
- ☐ Horseback Riding
- ☐ Hunting
- ☐ Kayaking

- ☐ Marina
- ☐ Nature Center
- ☐ Photography
- ☐ Swimming
- ☐ Waterfalls
- ☐ Watersports
- ☐ Wildlife & Birding
- ☐ Winter Sports
- ☐

Facilities:

- ☐ ADA
- ☐ Gift Shop
- ☐ Museum
- ☐ Visitor Center
- ☐ Restrooms

- ☐ Playground
- ☐ Picnic sites
- ☐
- ☐
- ☐

Memories of the Trip

Get the Facts

- ☐ Phone   (631) 669-0449
- ☐ Park Hours

  _____

- ☐ Reservations? _____ Y _____ N

  date made_____

- ☐ Open all year? _____ Y _____ N

  dates_____

- ☐ Dog friendly _____ Y _____ N

- ☐ Distance from home

  miles: _____

  hours: _____

- ☐ Address_____

  _____

  _____

Fees:

- ☐ Day Use $ _____
- ☐ Refund policy

  _____

  _____

  _____

Stamps & Stickers

Captree State Park

City: Bay Shore   County: Suffolk

Plan your trip: https://parks.ny.gov/parks/captree/details.aspx

Activities: (check all that apply)

- ❏ Beach
- ❏ Biking
- ❏ Boating
- ❏ Canoeing
- ❏ Fishing / Ice
- ❏ Hiking
- ❏ Horseback Riding
- ❏ Hunting
- ❏ Kayaking

- ❏ Marina
- ❏ Nature Center
- ❏ Photography
- ❏ Swimming
- ❏ Waterfalls
- ❏ Watersports
- ❏ Wildlife & Birding
- ❏ Winter Sports
- ❏

Facilities:

- ❏ ADA
- ❏ Gift Shop
- ❏ Museum
- ❏ Visitor Center
- ❏ Restrooms

- ❏ Playground
- ❏ Picnic sites
- ❏
- ❏
- ❏

Memories of the Trip

Get the Facts

- ❏ Phone   (631) 669-0449
- ❏ Park Hours

  _____

- ❏ Reservations? _____Y _____N

  date made_____

- ❏ Open all year? _____Y_____N

  dates_____

- ❏ Dog friendly _____Y _____N

- ❏ Distance from home

  miles: _____

  hours: _____

- ❏ Address_____

  _____

  _____

Fees:

- ❏ Day Use $ _____
- ❏ Refund policy

  _____

  _____

  _____

Stamps & Stickers

Brentwood State Park
City: Brentwood   County: Suffolk

Plan your trip: https://parks.ny.gov/parks/brentwood/details.aspx

Activities: (check all that apply)

- ❑ Beach
- ❑ Biking
- ❑ Boating
- ❑ Canoeing
- ❑ Fishing / Ice
- ❑ Hiking
- ❑ Horseback Riding
- ❑ Hunting
- ❑ Kayaking

- ❑ Marina
- ❑ Nature Center
- ❑ Photography
- ❑ Swimming
- ❑ Waterfalls
- ❑ Watersports
- ❑ Wildlife & Birding
- ❑ Winter Sports
- ❑

Facilities:

- ❑ ADA
- ❑ Gift Shop
- ❑ Museum
- ❑ Visitor Center
- ❑ Restrooms

- ❑ Playground
- ❑ Picnic sites
- ❑
- ❑
- ❑

Memories of the Trip

Get the Facts

- ❑ Phone   (631) 667-5055
- ❑ Park Hours

  _____

- ❑ Reservations? ____Y ____N

  date made_____

- ❑ Open all year? ____Y____N

  dates_____

- ❑ Dog friendly ـ____Y ____N

- ❑ Distance from home

  miles: _____

  hours: _____

- ❑ Address_____

  _____

  _____

Fees:

- ❑ Day Use $ _____
- ❑ Refund policy

  _____

  _____

  _____

Stamps & Stickers

Cold Spring Harbor State Park
City: Cold Spring Harbor   County: Suffolk

Plan your trip: https://parks.ny.gov/parks/coldspringharbor/details.aspx

Activities: (check all that apply)

- ❑ Beach
- ❑ Biking
- ❑ Boating
- ❑ Canoeing
- ❑ Fishing / Ice
- ❑ Hiking
- ❑ Horseback Riding
- ❑ Hunting
- ❑ Kayaking

- ❑ Marina
- ❑ Nature Center
- ❑ Photography
- ❑ Swimming
- ❑ Waterfalls
- ❑ Watersports
- ❑ Wildlife & Birding
- ❑ Winter Sports
- ❑

Facilities:

- ❑ ADA
- ❑ Gift Shop
- ❑ Museum
- ❑ Visitor Center
- ❑ Restrooms

- ❑ Playground
- ❑ Picnic sites
- ❑
- ❑
- ❑

Memories of the Trip

Get the Facts

- ❑ Phone   (631) 423-1770
- ❑ Park Hours

  _____

- ❑ Reservations? _____Y _____N

  date made_____

- ❑ Open all year? _____Y_____N

  dates_____

- ❑ Dog friendly _____Y _____N

- ❑ Distance from home

  miles: _____

  hours: _____

- ❑ Address_____

  _____

  _____

Fees:

- ❑ Day Use $ _____
- ❑ Refund policy

  _____

  _____

  _____

Stamps & Stickers

Bayard Cutting Arboretum State Park
City: Great River   County: Suffolk

Plan your trip: https://parks.ny.gov/parks/bayardcuttingarboretumn/details.aspx

Activities: (check all that apply)

- ❑ Beach
- ❑ Biking
- ❑ Boating
- ❑ Canoeing
- ❑ Fishing / Ice
- ❑ Hiking
- ❑ Horseback Riding
- ❑ Hunting
- ❑ Kayaking

- ❑ Marina
- ❑ Nature Center
- ❑ Photography
- ❑ Swimming
- ❑ Waterfalls
- ❑ Watersports
- ❑ Wildlife & Birding
- ❑ Winter Sports
- ❑

Facilities:

- ❑ ADA
- ❑ Gift Shop
- ❑ Museum
- ❑ Visitor Center
- ❑ Restrooms

- ❑ Playground
- ❑ Picnic sites
- ❑
- ❑
- ❑

Memories of the Trip

Get the Facts

- ❑ Phone   (631) 581-1002
- ❑ Park Hours

  _____

- ❑ Reservations? _____Y _____N

  date made_____

- ❑ Open all year? _____Y_____N

  dates_____

- ❑ Dog friendly _____Y _____N

- ❑ Distance from home

  miles: _____

  hours: _____

- ❑ Address_____

  _____

  _____

Fees:

- ❑ Day Use $ _____
- ❑ Refund policy

  _____

  _____

  _____

Stamps & Stickers

Nissequogue River State Park
City: Kings Park   County: Suffolk

Plan your trip: https://parks.ny.gov/parks/nissequogueriver/details.aspx

Activities: (check all that apply)

- ❑ Beach
- ❑ Biking
- ❑ Boating
- ❑ Canoeing
- ❑ Fishing / Ice
- ❑ Hiking
- ❑ Horseback Riding
- ❑ Hunting
- ❑ Kayaking

- ❑ Marina
- ❑ Nature Center
- ❑ Photography
- ❑ Swimming
- ❑ Waterfalls
- ❑ Watersports
- ❑ Wildlife & Birding
- ❑ Winter Sports
- ❑

Facilities:

- ❑ ADA
- ❑ Gift Shop
- ❑ Museum
- ❑ Visitor Center
- ❑ Restrooms

- ❑ Playground
- ❑ Picnic sites
- ❑
- ❑
- ❑

Memories of the Trip

Get the Facts

- ❑ Phone   (631) 269-4927
- ❑ Park Hours

    _____

- ❑ Reservations? ____Y ____N

    date made_____

- ❑ Open all year? ____Y____N

    dates_____

- ❑ Dog friendly ____Y ____N

- ❑ Distance from home

    miles: _____

    hours: _____

- ❑ Address_____

    _____

    _____

Fees:

- ❑ Day Use $ _____
- ❑ Refund policy

    _____

    _____

    _____

Stamps & Stickers

Sunken Meadow State Park
City: Kings Park   County: Suffolk

Plan your trip: https://parks.ny.gov/parks/sunkenmeadow/details.aspx

Activities: (check all that apply)

- ❑ Beach
- ❑ Biking
- ❑ Boating
- ❑ Canoeing
- ❑ Fishing / Ice
- ❑ Hiking
- ❑ Horseback Riding
- ❑ Hunting
- ❑ Kayaking

- ❑ Marina
- ❑ Nature Center
- ❑ Photography
- ❑ Swimming
- ❑ Waterfalls
- ❑ Watersports
- ❑ Wildlife & Birding
- ❑ Winter Sports
- ❑

Facilities:

- ❑ ADA
- ❑ Gift Shop
- ❑ Museum
- ❑ Visitor Center
- ❑ Restrooms

- ❑ Playground
- ❑ Picnic sites
- ❑
- ❑
- ❑

Memories of the Trip

Get the Facts

- ❑ Phone   (631) 269-4333
- ❑ Park Hours

_____

- ❑ Reservations? _____Y _____N

date made_____

- ❑ Open all year? _____Y_____N

dates_____

- ❑ Dog friendly _____Y _____N

- ❑ Distance from home

miles: _____

hours: _____

- ❑ Address_____

_____

_____

Fees:

- ❑ Day Use $ _____
- ❑ Refund policy

_____

_____

_____

Stamps & Stickers

Camp Hero State Park
City: Montauk   County: Suffolk

Plan your trip: https://parks.ny.gov/parks/camphero/details.aspx

Activities: (check all that apply)

- ❑ Beach
- ❑ Biking
- ❑ Boating
- ❑ Canoeing
- ❑ Fishing / Ice
- ❑ Hiking
- ❑ Horseback Riding
- ❑ Hunting
- ❑ Kayaking

- ❑ Marina
- ❑ Nature Center
- ❑ Photography
- ❑ Swimming
- ❑ Waterfalls
- ❑ Watersports
- ❑ Wildlife & Birding
- ❑ Winter Sports
- ❑

Facilities:

- ❑ ADA
- ❑ Gift Shop
- ❑ Museum
- ❑ Visitor Center
- ❑ Restrooms

- ❑ Playground
- ❑ Picnic sites
- ❑
- ❑
- ❑

Memories of the Trip

Get the Facts

- ❑ Phone   (631) 668-3781
- ❑ Park Hours

  _____

- ❑ Reservations? ____Y ____N

  date made_____

- ❑ Open all year? ____Y____N

  dates_____

- ❑ Dog friendly _____Y _____N

- ❑ Distance from home

  miles: _____

  hours: _____

- ❑ Address_____

  _____

  _____

Fees:

- ❑ Day Use $ _____
- ❑ Refund policy

  _____

  _____

  _____

Stamps & Stickers

Montauk Downs State Park
City: Montauk   County: Suffolk

Plan your trip: https://parks.ny.gov/parks/montaukdowns/details.aspx

Activities: (check all that apply)

- ❑ Beach
- ❑ Biking
- ❑ Boating
- ❑ Canoeing
- ❑ Fishing / Ice
- ❑ Hiking
- ❑ Horseback Riding
- ❑ Hunting
- ❑ Kayaking

- ❑ Marina
- ❑ Nature Center
- ❑ Photography
- ❑ Swimming
- ❑ Waterfalls
- ❑ Watersports
- ❑ Wildlife & Birding
- ❑ Winter Sports
- ❑

Facilities:

- ❑ ADA
- ❑ Gift Shop
- ❑ Museum
- ❑ Visitor Center
- ❑ Restrooms

- ❑ Playground
- ❑ Picnic sites
- ❑
- ❑
- ❑

Memories of the Trip

Get the Facts

- ❑ Phone   (631) 668-3781
- ❑ Park Hours

_____

- ❑ Reservations? ____Y ____N

date made_____

- ❑ Open all year? ____Y____N

dates_____

- ❑ Dog friendly _____Y _____N

- ❑ Distance from home

miles: _____

hours: _____

- ❑ Address_____

_____

_____

Fees:

- ❑ Day Use $ _____
- ❑ Refund policy

_____

_____

_____

Stamps & Stickers

Montauk Point State Park

City: Montauk　　　　County: Suffolk

Plan your trip: https://parks.ny.gov/parks/montaukpoint/details.aspx

Activities: (check all that apply)

- ❏ Beach
- ❏ Biking
- ❏ Boating
- ❏ Canoeing
- ❏ Fishing / Ice
- ❏ Hiking
- ❏ Horseback Riding
- ❏ Hunting
- ❏ Kayaking

- ❏ Marina
- ❏ Nature Center
- ❏ Photography
- ❏ Swimming
- ❏ Waterfalls
- ❏ Watersports
- ❏ Wildlife & Birding
- ❏ Winter Sports
- ❏

Facilities:

- ❏ ADA
- ❏ Gift Shop
- ❏ Museum
- ❏ Visitor Center
- ❏ Restrooms

- ❏ Playground
- ❏ Picnic sites
- ❏
- ❏
- ❏

Get the Facts

- ❏ Phone　(631) 668-3781
- ❏ Park Hours

　_____

- ❏ Reservations? ____Y ____N

　date made_____

- ❏ Open all year? ____Y____N

　dates_____

- ❏ Dog friendly _____Y _____N
- ❏ Distance from home

　miles: _____

　hours: _____

- ❏ Address_____

　_____

　_____

Fees:

- ❏ Day Use $ _____
- ❏ Refund policy

　_____

　_____

　_____

Stamps & Stickers

Memories of the Trip

Shadmoor State Park

City: Montauk   County: Suffolk

Plan your trip: https://parks.ny.gov/parks/shadmoor/details.aspx

Activities: (check all that apply)

- ❑ Beach
- ❑ Biking
- ❑ Boating
- ❑ Canoeing
- ❑ Fishing / Ice
- ❑ Hiking
- ❑ Horseback Riding
- ❑ Hunting
- ❑ Kayaking

- ❑ Marina
- ❑ Nature Center
- ❑ Photography
- ❑ Swimming
- ❑ Waterfalls
- ❑ Watersports
- ❑ Wildlife & Birding
- ❑ Winter Sports
- ❑

Facilities:

- ❑ ADA
- ❑ Gift Shop
- ❑ Museum
- ❑ Visitor Center
- ❑ Restrooms

- ❑ Playground
- ❑ Picnic sites
- ❑
- ❑
- ❑

Memories of the Trip

Get the Facts

- ❑ Phone   (631) 668-3781
- ❑ Park Hours

  _____

- ❑ Reservations? _____Y _____N

  date made_____

- ❑ Open all year? _____Y_____N

  dates_____

- ❑ Dog friendly _____Y _____N

- ❑ Distance from home

  miles: _____

  hours: _____

- ❑ Address_____

  _____

  _____

Fees:

- ❑ Day Use $ _____
- ❑ Refund policy

  _____

  _____

  _____

Stamps & Stickers

Belmont Lake State Park
City: North Babylon   County: Suffolk

Plan your trip: https://parks.ny.gov/parks/belmontlake/details.aspx

Activities: (check all that apply)

- ❏ Beach
- ❏ Biking
- ❏ Boating
- ❏ Canoeing
- ❏ Fishing / Ice
- ❏ Hiking
- ❏ Horseback Riding
- ❏ Hunting
- ❏ Kayaking

- ❏ Marina
- ❏ Nature Center
- ❏ Photography
- ❏ Swimming
- ❏ Waterfalls
- ❏ Watersports
- ❏ Wildlife & Birding
- ❏ Winter Sports
- ❏

Facilities:

- ❏ ADA
- ❏ Gift Shop
- ❏ Museum
- ❏ Visitor Center
- ❏ Restrooms

- ❏ Playground
- ❏ Picnic sites
- ❏
- ❏
- ❏

Memories of the Trip

Get the Facts

- ❏ Phone   (631) 667-5055
- ❏ Park Hours

  _____

- ❏ Reservations? ____Y ____N

  date made_____
- ❏ Open all year? ____Y____N

  dates_____
- ❏ Dog friendly _____Y _____N
- ❏ Distance from home

  miles: _____

  hours: _____
- ❏ Address_____

  _____

  _____

Fees:

- ❏ Day Use $ _____
- ❏ Refund policy

  _____

  _____

  _____

Stamps & Stickers

Connetquot River State Park Preserve

City: Oakdale   County: Suffolk

Plan your trip: https://parks.ny.gov/parks/connetquotriver/details.aspx

Activities: (check all that apply)

- ❑ Beach
- ❑ Biking
- ❑ Boating
- ❑ Canoeing
- ❑ Fishing / Ice
- ❑ Hiking
- ❑ Horseback Riding
- ❑ Hunting
- ❑ Kayaking

- ❑ Marina
- ❑ Nature Center
- ❑ Photography
- ❑ Swimming
- ❑ Waterfalls
- ❑ Watersports
- ❑ Wildlife & Birding
- ❑ Winter Sports
- ❑

Facilities:

- ❑ ADA
- ❑ Gift Shop
- ❑ Museum
- ❑ Visitor Center
- ❑ Restrooms

- ❑ Playground
- ❑ Picnic sites
- ❑
- ❑
- ❑

Memories of the Trip

Get the Facts

- ❑ Phone   (631) 581-1005
- ❑ Park Hours

  _____

- ❑ Reservations? _____ Y _____ N

  date made_____

- ❑ Open all year? _____ Y _____ N

  dates_____

- ❑ Dog friendly _____ Y _____ N

- ❑ Distance from home

  miles: _____

  hours: _____

- ❑ Address_____

  _____

  _____

Fees:

- ❑ Day Use $ _____
- ❑ Refund policy

  _____

  _____

  _____

Stamps & Stickers

Orient Beach State Park
City: Orient   County: Suffolk

Plan your trip: https://parks.ny.gov/parks/orientbeach/details.aspx

Activities: (check all that apply)

- ❑ Beach
- ❑ Biking
- ❑ Boating
- ❑ Canoeing
- ❑ Fishing / Ice
- ❑ Hiking
- ❑ Horseback Riding
- ❑ Hunting
- ❑ Kayaking

- ❑ Marina
- ❑ Nature Center
- ❑ Photography
- ❑ Swimming
- ❑ Waterfalls
- ❑ Watersports
- ❑ Wildlife & Birding
- ❑ Winter Sports
- ❑

Facilities:

- ❑ ADA
- ❑ Gift Shop
- ❑ Museum
- ❑ Visitor Center
- ❑ Restrooms

- ❑ Playground
- ❑ Picnic sites
- ❑
- ❑
- ❑

Memories of the Trip

Get the Facts

- ❑ Phone   (631) 323-2440
- ❑ Park Hours

  _____

- ❑ Reservations? ____Y ____N

  date made_____

- ❑ Open all year? ____Y____N

  dates_____

- ❑ Dog friendly _____Y _____N

- ❑ Distance from home

  miles: _____

  hours: _____

- ❑ Address_____

  _____

  _____

Fees:

- ❑ Day Use $ _____
- ❑ Refund policy

  _____

  _____

  _____

Stamps & Stickers

Brookhaven State Park

City: Ridge　　　　　　County: Suffolk

Plan your trip: https://parks.ny.gov/parks/brookhaven/details.aspx

Activities: (check all that apply)

- ❑ Beach
- ❑ Biking
- ❑ Boating
- ❑ Canoeing
- ❑ Fishing / Ice
- ❑ Hiking
- ❑ Horseback Riding
- ❑ Hunting
- ❑ Kayaking

- ❑ Marina
- ❑ Nature Center
- ❑ Photography
- ❑ Swimming
- ❑ Waterfalls
- ❑ Watersports
- ❑ Wildlife & Birding
- ❑ Winter Sports
- ❑

Facilities:

- ❑ ADA
- ❑ Gift Shop
- ❑ Museum
- ❑ Visitor Center
- ❑ Restrooms

- ❑ Playground
- ❑ Picnic sites
- ❑
- ❑
- ❑

Memories of the Trip

Get the Facts

- ❑ Phone　(631) 929-4314
- ❑ Park Hours

  _____

- ❑ Reservations? ____Y ____N

  date made_____

- ❑ Open all year? ____Y____N

  dates_____

- ❑ Dog friendly _____Y _____N

- ❑ Distance from home

  miles: _____

  hours: _____

- ❑ Address_____

  _____

  _____

Fees:

- ❑ Day Use $ _____
- ❑ Refund policy

  _____

  _____

  _____

Stamps & Stickers

Hallock State Park Preserve
City: Riverhead   County: Suffolk

Plan your trip: https://parks.ny.gov/parks/hallock/details.aspx

Activities: (check all that apply)

- ❑ Beach
- ❑ Biking
- ❑ Boating
- ❑ Canoeing
- ❑ Fishing / Ice
- ❑ Hiking
- ❑ Horseback Riding
- ❑ Hunting
- ❑ Kayaking

- ❑ Marina
- ❑ Nature Center
- ❑ Photography
- ❑ Swimming
- ❑ Waterfalls
- ❑ Watersports
- ❑ Wildlife & Birding
- ❑ Winter Sports
- ❑

Facilities:

- ❑ ADA
- ❑ Gift Shop
- ❑ Museum
- ❑ Visitor Center
- ❑ Restrooms

- ❑ Playground
- ❑ Picnic sites
- ❑
- ❑
- ❑

Memories of the Trip

Get the Facts

- ❑ Phone   (631) 315-5475
- ❑ Park Hours

_____

- ❑ Reservations? ____ Y ____ N

date made_____

- ❑ Open all year? ____ Y ____ N

dates_____

- ❑ Dog friendly _____ Y _____ N
- ❑ Distance from home

miles: _____

hours: _____

- ❑ Address_____

_____

_____

Fees:

- ❑ Day Use $ _____
- ❑ Refund policy

_____

_____

_____

Stamps & Stickers

Caleb Smith State Park Preserve

City: Smithtown   **County: Suffolk**

Plan your trip: https://parks.ny.gov/parks/calebsmith/details.aspx

Activities: (check all that apply)

- ❑ Beach
- ❑ Biking
- ❑ Boating
- ❑ Canoeing
- ❑ Fishing / Ice
- ❑ Hiking
- ❑ Horseback Riding
- ❑ Hunting
- ❑ Kayaking

- ❑ Marina
- ❑ Nature Center
- ❑ Photography
- ❑ Swimming
- ❑ Waterfalls
- ❑ Watersports
- ❑ Wildlife & Birding
- ❑ Winter Sports
- ❑

Facilities:

- ❑ ADA
- ❑ Gift Shop
- ❑ Museum
- ❑ Visitor Center
- ❑ Restrooms

- ❑ Playground
- ❑ Picnic sites
- ❑
- ❑
- ❑

Get the Facts

- ❑ Phone   (631) 265-1054
- ❑ Park Hours

  _____

- ❑ Reservations? _____Y _____N

  date made_____

- ❑ Open all year? _____Y_____N

  dates_____

- ❑ Dog friendly _____Y _____N

- ❑ Distance from home

  miles: _____

  hours: _____

- ❑ Address_____

  _____

  _____

Fees:

- ❑ Day Use $ _____
- ❑ Refund policy

  _____

  _____

  _____

Stamps & Stickers

Memories of the Trip

INDEX

RA: *Recreation Area Area* SMP: *State Marine Park* SP: *State Park* SPP: *State Park Preserve*

INDEX

RA: *Recreation Area Area* SMP: *State Marine Park* SP: *State Park* SPP: *State Park Preserve*